curriculum
mathematics
practice 1

C Oliver   A Ledsham   R Elvin   M Bindley

Oxford University Press

Oxford University Press, Great Clarendon Street, Oxford OX2 6DP

Oxford New York
Athens Auckland Bangkok Bogotá Buenos Aires
Calcutta Cape Town Chennai Dar es Salaam
Delhi Florence Hong Kong Istanbul Karachi
Kuala Lumpur Madrid Melbourne Mexico City
Mumbai Nairobi Paris São Paulo Shanghai
Singapore Taipei Tokyo Toronto Warsaw

and associated companies in

Berlin Ibadan

Oxford is a trade mark of Oxford University Press
© Oxford University Press 1996

Series first published as *Comprehensive Mathematics Practice* 1981
Updated edition of *Curriculum Mathematics Practice* first published 1996
Reprinted 1997, 1998, 1999, 2000

ISBN 0 19 833741 8
A CIP record for this book is available from the British Library.

Typeset and illustrated by Tech Set Ltd
Printed and bound in Great Britain by Butler and Tanner Ltd, Frome and London

Preface

Curriculum Mathematics Practice is an updated version of *Comprehensive Mathematics Practice*, a successful series designed for the majority of students in their first years of secondary schooling. As before, the books provide a vast range of carefully constructed and graded exercises in a coherent mathematical progression, with many of these exercises set in a real-life context. The levels targeted are 3–8, and details of how all six new books relate to the curriculum are given in the Answer Book.

These new books do not attempt to provide a complete scheme for the National Curriculum. No attempt has been made for instance to cover 'Using and Applying Mathematics' or computer work. It is expected, however, that mathematics departments will use other resources for those aspects (e.g. *Oxford Mathematics*) and that *Curriculum Mathematics Practice* will provide a core of skill practice within an overall scheme of work.

The series has the same objective as the original books. The series should enable students 'to gain confidence in their abilities and master the fundamental processes so necessary for future success'.

Mark Bindley
Revising Editor
December 1995

Contents

Unit 1 Place value

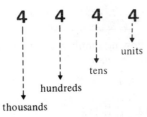

The number shown above is made up of
4 thousands, 4 hundreds, 4 tens and 4 units.
It is the number four thousand four hundred
and forty-four.
You will see that the value of each 4 depends
upon its position, that is its place value.

Example 1

Write down the following numbers in words.
a 234   **b** 6070

a two hundred and thirty-four
b six thousand and seventy

Exercise 1.1

Write the following numbers in words.

1 12	**2** 15	**3** 36	**4** 91
5 150	**6** 340	**7** 345	**8** 210
9 217	**10** 508	**11** 601	**12** 2300
13 2370	**14** 3670	**15** 3678	**16** 7210
17 7215	**18** 7203	**19** 4504	**20** 4024
21 3037	**22** 3030	**23** 8020	**24** 8007
25 9001			

26 Write in words:
   a the altitude of Beattock Summit,
   b its distance from Glasgow,
   c its distance from London.

27 Write in words the length of the Mersey Tunnel.

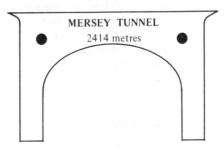

28 Write in words:
   a the distance from Liverpool to New York,
   b the distance from Southampton to Panama,
   c the distance from London to Cape Town.

Exercise 1.2

Write the following numbers in figures.

1 seventeen	**2** nineteen
3 forty-five	**4** seventy-three
5 one hundred and ninety	
6 four hundred and sixty	
7 four hundred and sixty-seven	
8 eight hundred and ten	
9 eight hundred and twelve	
10 seven hundred and four	
11 nine hundred and one	
12 six thousand five hundred	
13 six thousand five hundred and twenty	
14 nine thousand one hundred and thirty	
15 nine thousand one hundred and thirty-three	

16 three thousand six hundred and ten
17 three thousand six hundred and nineteen
18 three thousand six hundred and two
19 eight thousand seven hundred and six
20 eight thousand and ninety-one
21 one thousand and fifty-six
22 one thousand and fifty
23 four thousand and ten
24 four thousand and four
25 eight thousand and eleven

In questions **26** to **30** a number is written in a sentence. Rewrite the number in figures.

26 There are seven hundred and thirty-six pupils at Manor Hill School.
27 Queen Elizabeth II was crowned eight hundred and eighty-seven years after the Norman Conquest.
28 Nine thousand one hundred and twenty-one spectators were at the football match last Saturday.
29 The population of Leominster is seven thousand two hundred and six.
30 The summit of Snowdon is one thousand and eighty-five metres above sea level.

Example 2

Give the value of each underlined figure.
a 4$\underline{8}$3   **b** 2$\underline{0}$04

a eight tens or eighty
b 0 hundreds or 0

Exercise 1.3

Give the value of each underlined figure.

1	1$\underline{1}$	**2**	1$\underline{6}$	**3**	32$\underline{5}$	**4**	35$\underline{3}$
5	6$\underline{0}$7	**6**	4$\underline{3}$1	**7**	6$\underline{5}$0	**8**	$\underline{3}$31
9	$\underline{9}$80	**10**	$\underline{5}$01	**11**	437$\underline{6}$	**12**	9$\underline{2}$52
13	540$\underline{7}$	**14**	900$\underline{2}$	**15**	21$\underline{7}$5	**16**	35$\underline{1}$4
17	71$\underline{6}$0	**18**	80$\underline{5}$0	**19**	1$\underline{9}$37	**20**	3$\underline{1}$06
21	4$\underline{3}$00	**22**	5$\underline{2}$37	**23**	$\underline{8}$025	**24**	$\underline{1}$010
25	$\underline{9}$999						

Example 3

Arrange the following numbers in order of size, starting with the smallest.
273, forty-six, 9126, three thousand and two, 7

The order is: 7, 46, 273, 3002, 9126

Exercise 1.4

Arrange the following numbers in order of size, starting with the *smallest*.

1 70, 72, 71, 73, 75
2 45, 40, 55, 54, 50
3 132, 113, 123, 121, 112
4 112, 110, 109, 120, 99
5 432, 423, 412, 433, 421
6 five hundred and thirty, five hundred and forty, five hundred and five, five hundred and four, five hundred and thirty-four
7 seven hundred and eighty-six, six hundred and eighty-seven, six hundred and seventy-eight, seven hundred and sixty-eight, eight hundred and seventy-six
8 two thousand two hundred and thirty-one, two thousand three hundred and twenty-one, two thousand one hundred and twenty-three, two thousand one hundred and thirty-two, two thousand three hundred and twelve
9 one thousand and sixty-one, one thousand and sixteen, one thousand one hundred and six, one thousand and six, one thousand and sixty
10 four thousand and forty, four thousand four hundred and four, four thousand and four, four thousand four hundred, four thousand and forty-four
11 eighty-eight, 99, 98, 89, ninety
12 180, one hundred and eight, 88, eighty, one hundred and eighteen
13 113, one hundred and thirty, 133, one hundred and three, 123
14 250, two hundred and twenty, two hundred and fifteen, 225, two hundred and fifty-five
15 606, six hundred and sixty, 665, six hundred and five, 650

Arrange the following numbers in order of size, starting with the *largest*.

16 forty-five, 55, fifty-six, 54, 44
17 ninety-nine, 109, one hundred and nineteen, 94, one hundred and four
18 105, one hundred and fifty, 120, one hundred and twenty-five, 155
19 330, three hundred and thirty-two, three hundred and fifty, 352, three hundred and forty-two
20 440, four hundred and four, 444, 414, four hundred and forty-one

Example 4

Give the largest and smallest numbers that can be made using *all* the following digits.

a 3, 8, 6 and 1   **b** 9, 0, 1 and 9

a Largest is 8631; smallest is 1368.
b Largest is 9910; smallest is 1099.

Exercise 1.5

Give the largest and smallest numbers that can be made using *all* the following digits.

1 3, 5 and 2		**2** 4, 9 and 3	
3 6, 8 and 1		**4** 5, 3 and 5	
5 7, 6 and 0		**6** 4, 3, 6 and 5	
7 4, 1, 9 and 7		**8** 2, 8, 1 and 5	
9 5, 1, 1 and 7		**10** 6, 3, 3 and 6	
11 3, 5, 0 and 2		**12** 9, 7, 0 and 0	

You can multiply a number by 10 by moving each figure one place to the left and putting nought in the empty units space.

So **a** $3 \times 10 = 3$ tens and 0 units $= 30$

   b $406 \times 10 = 4060$

Th	H	T	U		Th	H	T	U
	4	0	6			4	0	6	0

Exercise 1.6

Multiply each of these numbers by 10.

1 4	**2** 7	**3** 15	**4** 19
5 10	**6** 24	**7** 43	**8** 52
9 69	**10** 20	**11** 50	**12** 126
13 155	**14** 317	**15** 632	**16** 510
17 850	**18** 700	**19** 2317	**20** 3547
21 4620	**22** 7050	**23** 5300	**24** 8000
25 9901			

You can divide a number by 10 by moving each figure one place to the right; the units figure becomes the remainder.

So **a** $50 \div 10 = 5$ with a remainder of 0.
       i.e. 5

   b $632 \div 10 = 63$ with a remainder of 2.
       i.e. 63 r 2

Exercise 1.7

Divide each of these numbers by 10.

1 30	**2** 50	**3** 70	**4** 65
5 54	**6** 73	**7** 120	**8** 160
9 370	**10** 820	**11** 200	**12** 900
13 445	**14** 638	**15** 307	**16** 402
17 1320	**18** 4780	**19** 2300	**20** 5200
21 7000	**22** 5176	**23** 3078	**24** 4204
25 9001			

To multiply by 100, move each figure two places to the left.

So **a** $3 \times 100 = 300$

   b $406 \times 100 = 40\,600$

Exercise 1.8

Multiply each of these numbers by 100.

1 3	**2** 9	**3** 13	**4** 16
5 10	**6** 25	**7** 51	**8** 78
9 30	**10** 60	**11** 124	**12** 237
13 519	**14** 708	**15** 630	**16** 810
17 400	**18** 900	**19** 100	**20** 999

To divide by 100, move each figure two places to the right.

So **a** $500 \div 100 = 5$

   b $7263 \div 100 = 72$ r 63

Exercise 1.9

Divide each of these numbers by 100.

1 200	**2** 600	**3** 800	**4** 850
5 853	**6** 764	**7** 704	**8** 502
9 3200	**10** 9700	**11** 9710	**12** 4680
13 4683	**14** 5162	**15** 9375	**16** 4118
17 1384	**18** 3725	**19** 3705	**20** 5107
21 5007	**22** 2008	**23** 2030	**24** 8070

Exercise 1.10

1 Windows for this new building cost £54 each. What is the cost of providing windows for the front of the building?

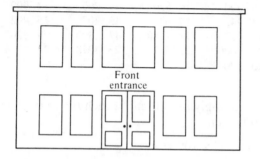

2 What is the height of the landing above the floor in **a** centimetres, **b** metres? (1 metre = 100 centimetres)

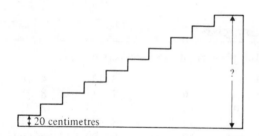

3 There are 100 kerb blocks between one end of Park Avenue and the other. What is the length of the avenue in **a** centimetres, **b** metres? (1 metre = 100 centimetres)

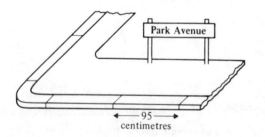

4 A teacher has 125 sheets of paper to share out amongst 10 pupils.
a How many sheets does each pupil receive?
b How many sheets does the teacher have left over?

5 A coal merchant has only 1318 bags of coal in his stock which he has to share out between 100 customers.
a How many bags can he supply to each customer?
b How many bags will he have left over?

Exercise 1.11

Copy the following and fill in the empty spaces.

1 $26 \times 10 =$		**2** $\quad \times 10 = 260$	
3 $26 \times \quad = 260$		**4** $260 \div 10 =$	
5 $\quad \div 10 = 26$		**6** $260 \div \quad = 26$	
7 $70 \times 10 =$		**8** $\quad \times 10 = 700$	
9 $70 \times \quad = 70$		**10** $700 \div 10 =$	
11 $\quad \div 10 = 70$		**12** $700 \div \quad = 70$	
13 $145 \times 10 =$		**14** $\quad \times 10 = 1450$	
15 $145 \times \quad = 1450$		**16** $1450 \div 10 =$	
17 $\quad \div 10 = 145$		**18** $1450 \div \quad = 145$	
19 $240 \times 10 =$		**20** $\quad \times 10 = 2400$	
21 $240 \times \quad = 2400$		**22** $2400 \div 10 =$	
23 $\quad \div 10 = 240$		**24** $2400 \div \quad = 240$	
25 $400 \times 10 =$		**26** $\quad \times 10 = 4000$	
27 $400 \times \quad = 4000$		**28** $4000 \div 10 =$	
29 $\quad \div 10 = 400$		**30** $4000 \div \quad = 400$	
31 $13 \times 100 =$		**32** $\quad \times 100 = 1300$	
33 $13 \times \quad = 1300$		**34** $1300 \div 100 =$	
35 $\quad \div 100 = 13$		**36** $1300 \div \quad = 13$	
37 $50 \times 100 =$		**38** $\quad \times 100 = 5000$	
39 $50 \times \quad = 5000$		**40** $5000 \div 100 =$	
41 $\quad \div 100 = 50$		**42** $5000 \div \quad = 50$	

Approximation

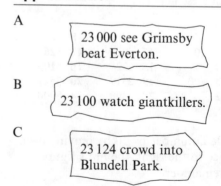

A

23 000 see Grimsby beat Everton.

B

23 100 watch giantkillers.

C

23 124 crowd into Blundell Park.

The numbers in each of these notices all give the attendance at the same football match.

A and B give an approximate or 'rounded off' attendance.

23 000 is the attendance to the nearest thousand.

23 100 is the attendance to the nearest hundred.

Certain rules are followed when 'rounding off'; these are shown below.

a 16 is nearer to 20 than it is to 10:
we say 16 = 20 *to the nearest ten.*
This is 'rounding up'.

b 24 is nearer to 20 than it is to 30:
we say 24 = 20 *to the nearest ten.*
This is 'rounding down'.

c 15 is halfway between 10 and 20; the number is usually 'rounded up':
we say 15 = 20 *to the nearest ten.*

Example 5

Give 1636   **a** to the nearest ten
           b to the nearest hundred
           c to the nearest thousand

a 36 is nearer to 40 than it is to 30;
so 1636 = 1640 to the nearest ten.

b 636 is nearer to 600 than it is to 700;
so 1636 = 1600 to the nearest hundred.

c 1636 is nearer to 2000 than it is to 1000;
so 1636 = 2000 to the nearest thousand.

Exercise 1.12

For questions **1** to **25**, give each number to the nearest ten.

1	32	**2**	54	**3**	48	**4**	76	**5**	21
6	93	**7**	89	**8**	17	**9**	8	**10**	65
11	35	**12**	98	**13**	167	**14**	149	**15**	153
16	321	**17**	536	**18**	278	**19**	109	**20**	612
21	474	**22**	103	**23**	196	**24**	185	**25**	305

For questions **26** to **35**, give each number to the nearest hundred.

		a		b		c
26	a	180	b	389	c	483
27	a	260	b	568	c	662
28	a	120	b	322	c	527
29	a	310	b	413	c	719
30	a	240	b	141	c	548
31	a	670	b	874	c	477
32	a	590	b	693	c	995
33	a	850	b	755	c	545
34	a	930	b	835	c	634
35	a	104	b	210	c	308

For questions **36** to **43**, give each number to the nearest ten.

36	1642	**37**	3484	**38**	7278	**39**	2846
40	4563	**41**	6725	**42**	1598	**43**	5097

For questions **44** to **50**, give each number to the nearest hundred.

44	1870	**45**	7396	**46**	5430	**47**	2712
48	6168	**49**	3250	**50**	2980		

For questions **51** to **57**, give each number to the nearest thousand.

51	1700	**52**	2890	**53**	3200	**54**	6321
55	4978	**56**	8500	**57**	5555		

For questions **58** to **70**, give each number
a to the nearest ten
b to the nearest hundred
c to the nearest thousand

58	1687	**59**	3478	**60**	2139	**61**	4312
62	3724	**63**	5861	**64**	2568	**65**	1356
66	7425	**67**	2607	**68**	3802	**69**	4078
70	8029						

Unit 2 Line symmetry

If you can fold a shape down the middle so that one half fits exactly over the other, then the shape is said to be *symmetrical*. The fold line is called its *axis of symmetry*.

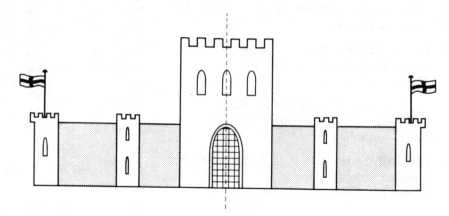

Example 1

Which one of the following shapes is different from the others, that is to say, not symmetrical?

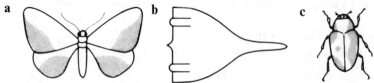

The one that is different is **c** because the left-hand side is not exactly the same as the right-hand side.

Exercise 2.1

For each of the following find which shape is different from the others, i.e. not symmetrical.

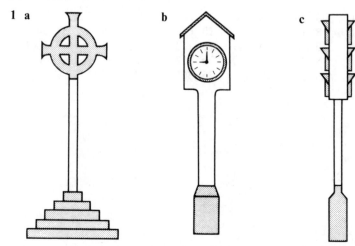

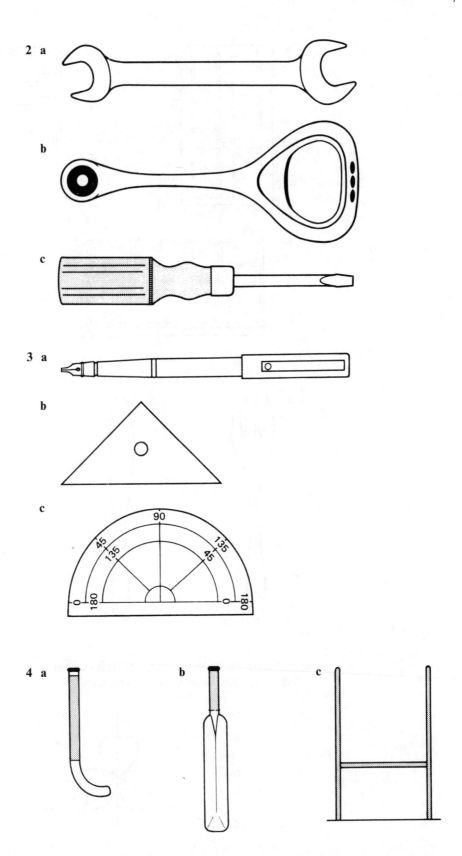

2 a

b

c

3 a

b

c

4 a   b   c

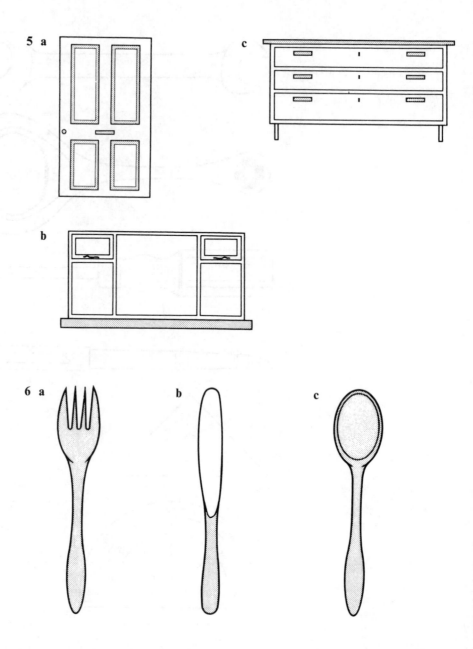

Some shapes have more than one axis of symmetry. For example a three-leafed clover has three lines of symmetry.

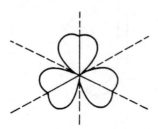

Example 2

Which one of the following shapes is different from the others, i.e. has only one line of symmetry?

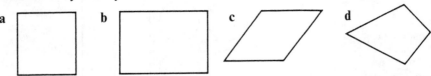

The one that is different is **d** because it has only one line of symmetry as shown in the diagram below.

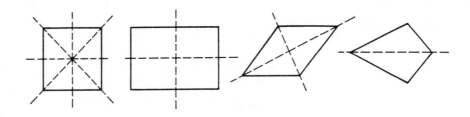

Exercise 2.2

For each of the following, find which shape is different from the others, i.e. has only one line of symmetry.

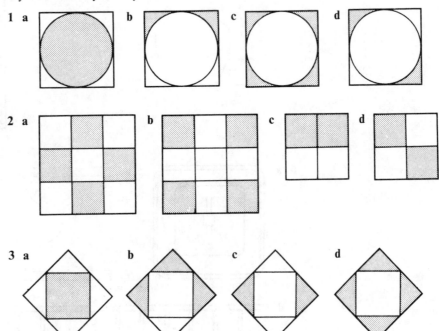

10

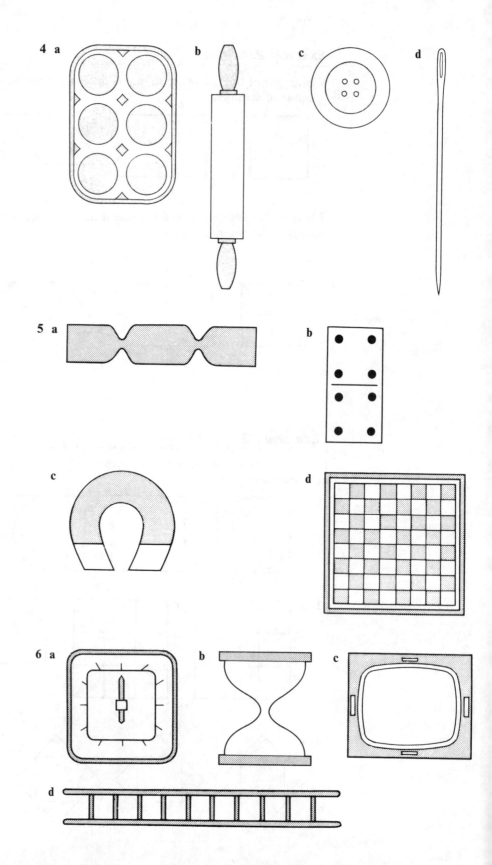

Solid objects can also be symmetrical, if you can slice them down the middle so that one half is a mirror image of the other. The slicing surface is called a *plane of symmetry*.

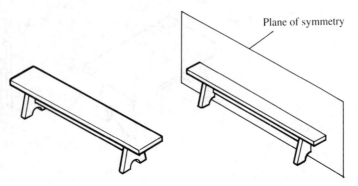

Example 3

Which of the following objects is different from the others, i.e. not symmetrical?

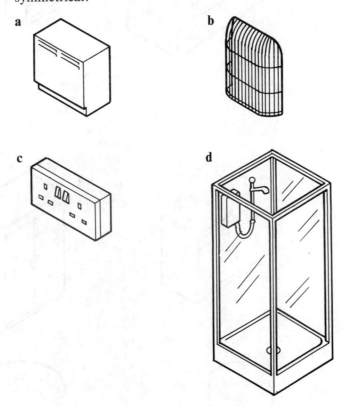

The one that is different is **d** because the shower cannot be sliced into two exact mirror images with a plane of symmetry.

12

For each of the following find which object is different from the others, i.e. not symmetrical.

1 a    b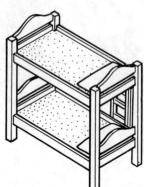

c 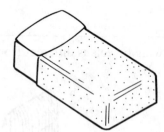   d

2 a 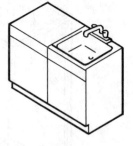   b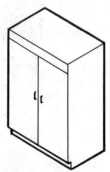

c   d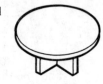

3 a

b

c

d

4 a

b

c

d

5 a

b

c

d

6 a

b

c

d

Reflection

To *reflect* a shape in a mirror line we go through these steps:
a imagine the mirror line is a line of symmetry.
b draw in a second shape (called the *image*) which makes the completed diagram symmetrical.

Example 4

In the following, the mirror line is shown by a broken line.
Copy each diagram on to squared paper or graph paper. Then draw the image formed by reflection in the mirror line.

a

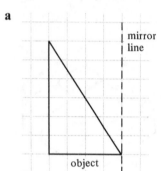
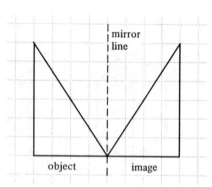

b

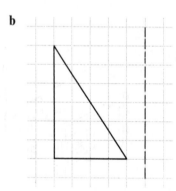
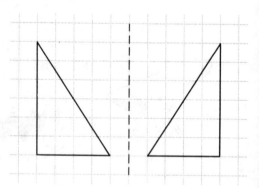

c

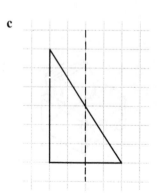
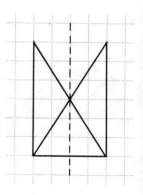

d

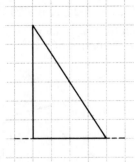

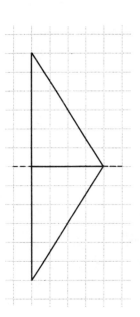

e

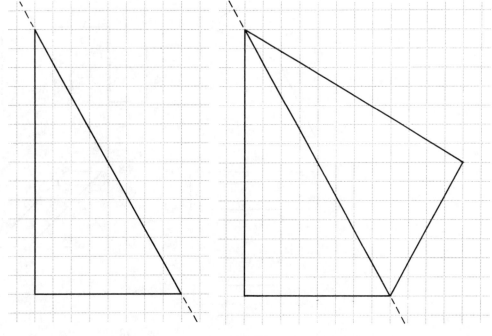

Exercise 2.4

Copy each of the following on to squared paper or graph paper. Then draw the image formed by reflection in the mirror line.

1

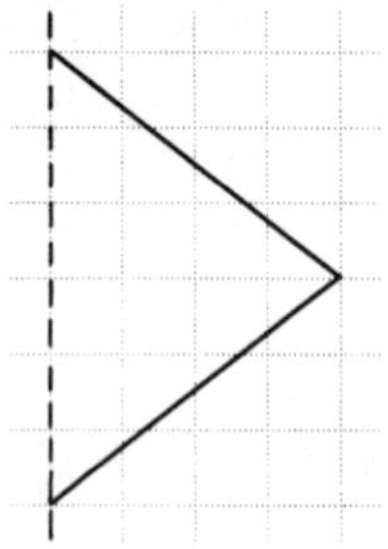

2

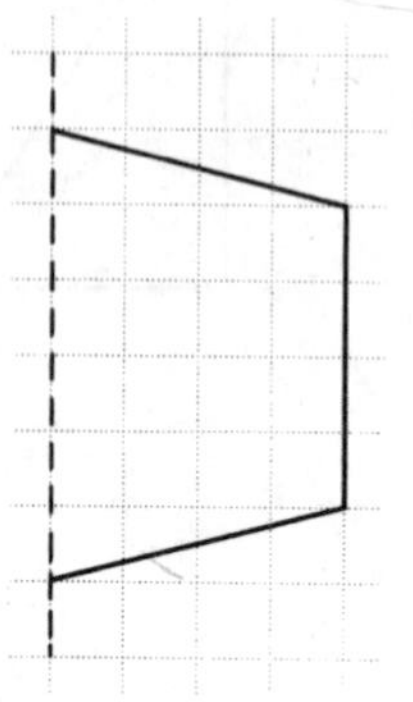

3

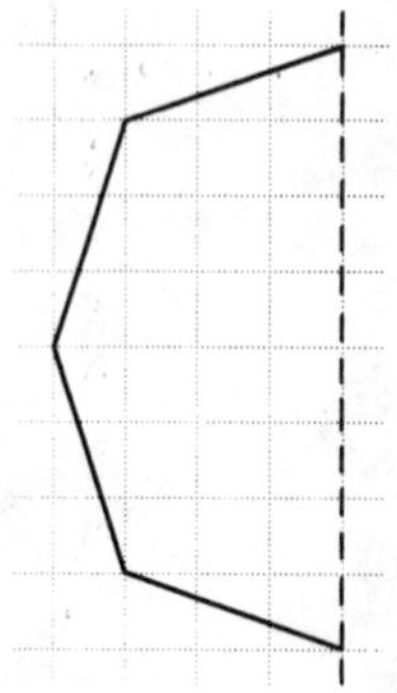

4

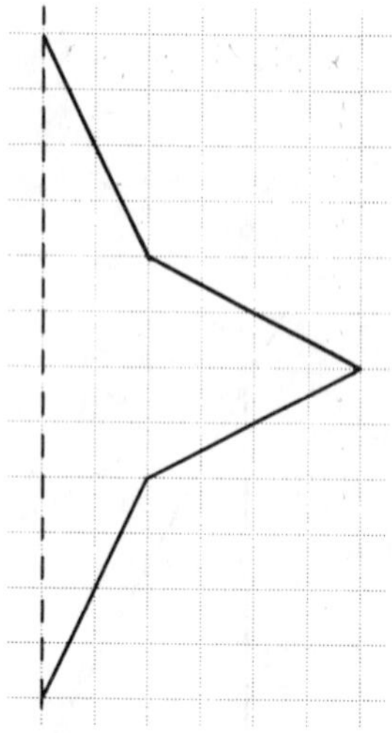

5

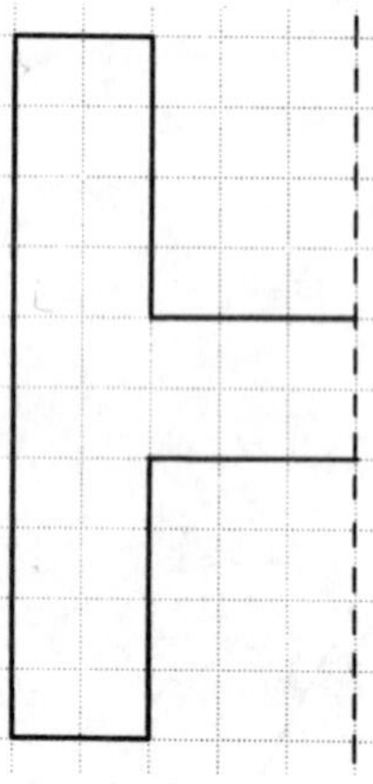

6

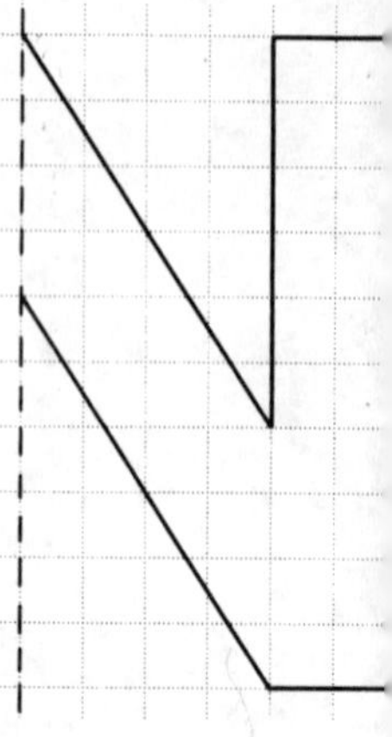

7

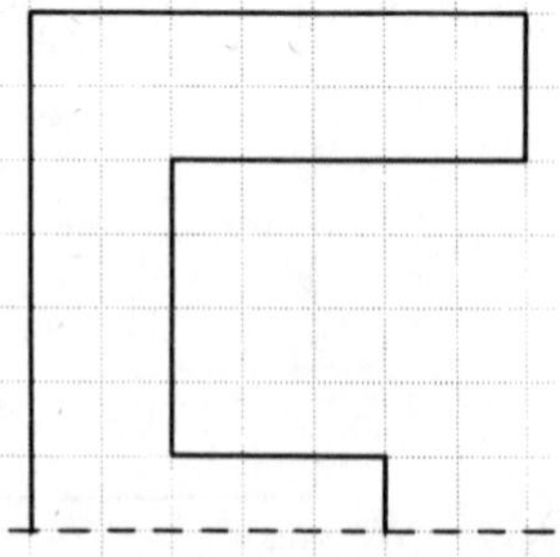

8

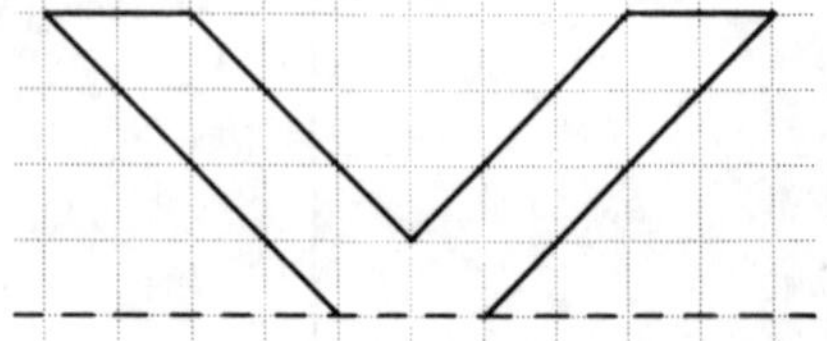

9

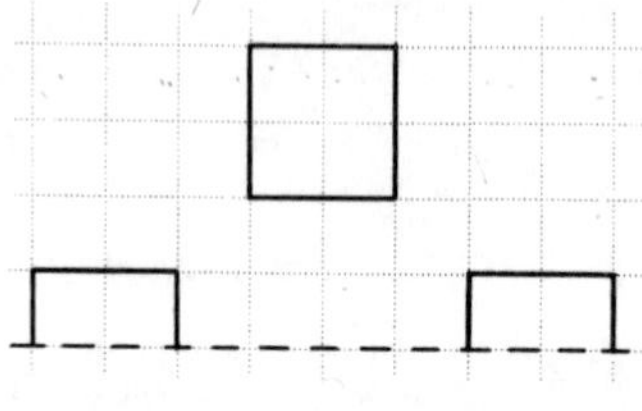

10

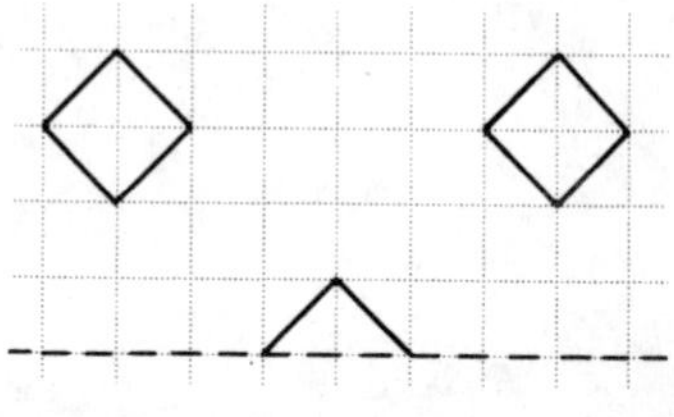

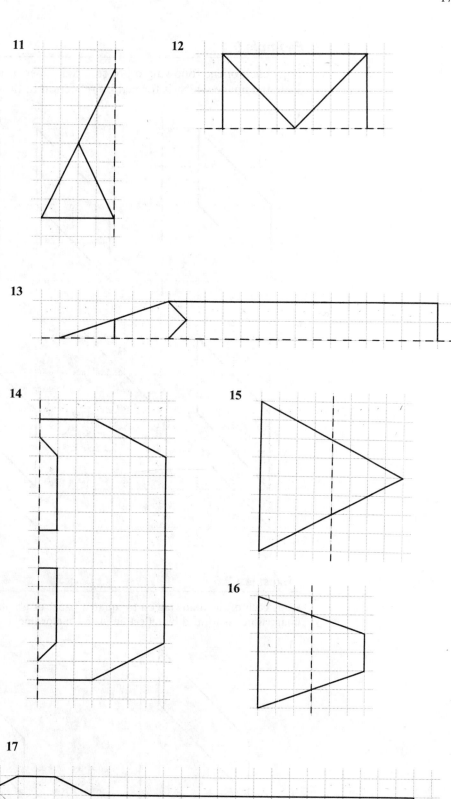

11

12

13

14

15

16

17

Example 5

Copy each of the following on to squared paper or graph paper and then draw the image which is formed by reflection in the mirror line.

a

b

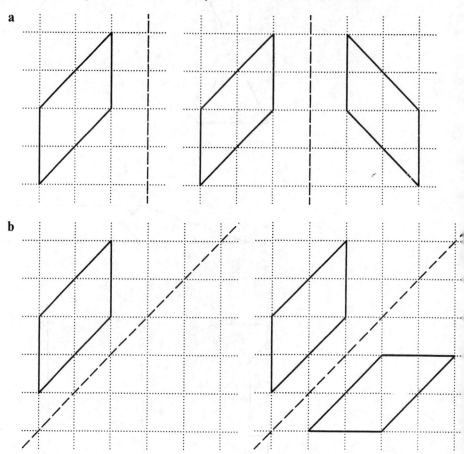

Copy each of the following on to squared paper or graph paper and then draw the image which is formed by reflection in the mirror line.

1

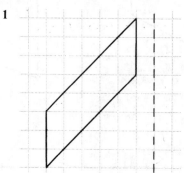

2

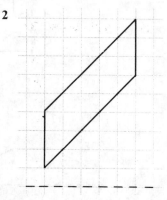

3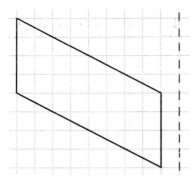

4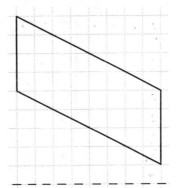

5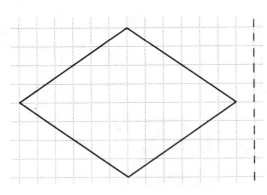

6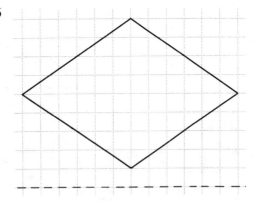

7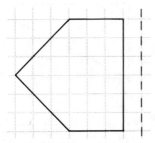

8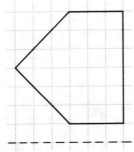

9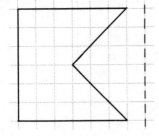

10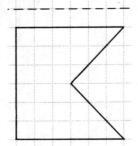

20

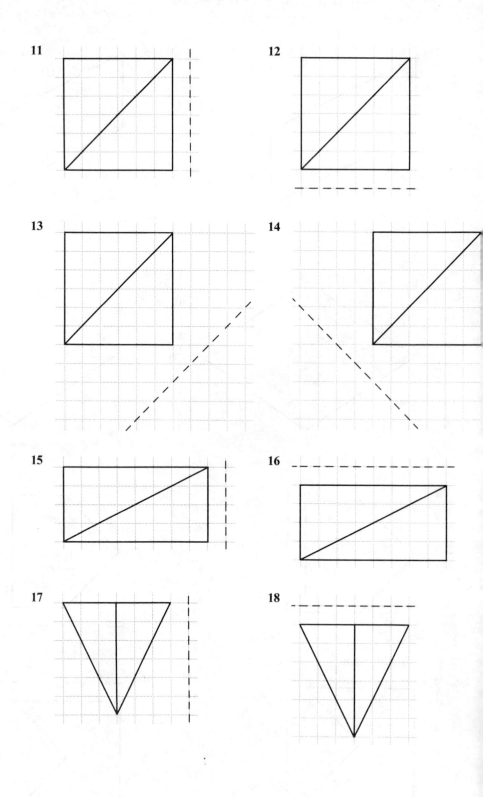

Unit 3 Adding and subtracting

Adding

Example 1

Add the following 'in your head' to find the 'odd answer out'.

a 16 + 22   b 27 + 11
c 22 + 19   d 19 + 19

This is one way to think the problems through:

a $16 + 22 = 10 + 6 + 20 + 2 = 30 + 8 = 38$

b $27 + 11 = 20 + 7 + 10 + 1 = 30 + 8 = 38$

c $22 + 19 = 20 + 2 + 10 + 9 = 30 + 11 = 41$

d $19 + 19 = 10 + 9 + 10 + 9 = 20 + 18 = 38$

So **c** has the 'odd answer out' because its answer is 41.

Exercise 3.1

Add the following 'in your head' to find the 'odd answer out'.

1	**a** 12 + 7		**b** 11 + 8	
	c 13 + 7		**d** 14 + 5	
2	**a** 14 + 14		**b** 13 + 15	
	c 19 + 9		**d** 14 + 15	
3	**a** 18 + 8		**b** 16 + 12	
	c 17 + 9		**d** 13 + 13	
4	**a** 21 + 12		**b** 25 + 7	
	c 14 + 18		**d** 15 + 17	
5	**a** 25 + 18		**b** 27 + 17	
	c 20 + 23		**d** 22 + 21	
6	**a** 51 + 12		**b** 45 + 18	
	c 49 + 11		**d** 48 + 15	
7	**a** 23 + 27		**b** 34 + 17	
	c 37 + 13		**d** 34 + 16	
8	**a** 34 + 25		**b** 28 + 31	
	c 49 + 11		**d** 17 + 42	
9	**a** 43 + 35		**b** 59 + 19	
	c 54 + 25		**d** 26 + 52	
10	**a** 81 + 17		**b** 75 + 22	
	c 18 + 79		**d** 51 + 46	
11	**a** 62 + 55		**b** 66 + 51	
	c 28 + 89		**d** 19 + 99	

12	**a** 131 + 26		**b** 140 + 17	
	c 45 + 122		**d** 89 + 68	
13	**a** 70 + 56		**b** 68 + 59	
	c 34 + 92		**d** 108 + 18	
14	**a** 122 + 25		**b** 47 + 90	
	c 85 + 52		**d** 111 + 26	
15	**a** 68 + 77		**b** 81 + 84	
	c 96 + 49		**d** 48 + 97	
16	**a** 123 + 57		**b** 114 + 66	
	c 95 + 85		**d** 80 + 110	
17	**a** 100 + 125		**b** 136 + 89	
	c 183 + 44		**d** 131 + 94	
18	**a** 140 + 100		**b** 135 + 105	
	c 125 + 125		**d** 151 + 89	
19	**a** 120 + 140		**b** 165 + 95	
	c 155 + 105		**d** 256 + 84	
20	**a** 222 + 90		**b** 150 + 150	
	c 45 + 255		**d** 199 + 101	

Example 2

Add the following to find the 'odd answer out'.

a $6 + 8 + 4 + 2$ b $7 + 2 + 9 + 3$
c $6 + 4 + 5 + 6$ d $8 + 1 + 5 + 7$

a		**b**		**c**		**d**	
	6		7		6		8
	8		2		4		1
	4		9		5		5
+	2	+	3	+	6	+	7
	20		**21**		**21**		**21**

So **a** has the 'odd answer out' because its answer is 20.

Exercise 3.2

Add the following to find the 'odd answer out'.

1	**a**		**b**		**c**		**d**	
		2		7		8		4
		5		2		1		3
		3		3		6		7
	+	8	+	6	+	4	+	4

2	**a**		**b**		**c**		**d**	
		4		6		8		5
		3		2		1		7
		8		9		7		3
	+	7	+	5	+	6	+	8

3
a
```
   7
   8
   9
 + 3
```
b
```
   6
   8
   5
 + 7
```
c
```
   8
   4
   5
 + 9
```
d
```
   6
   9
   4
 + 7
```

4
a
```
   8
   7
   6
 + 3
```
b
```
   5
   9
   7
 + 4
```
c
```
   9
   2
   8
 + 5
```
d
```
   7
   5
   9
 + 3
```

5
a $9 + 6 + 7 + 7$
b $8 + 5 + 6 + 9$
c $7 + 9 + 4 + 8$
d $8 + 8 + 5 + 7$

6
a $8 + 9 + 7 + 6$
b $9 + 7 + 9 + 5$
c $9 + 8 + 8 + 5$
d $7 + 7 + 8 + 9$

7
a
```
   12
   13
   11
 + 13
```
b
```
   11
   15
   10
 + 12
```
c
```
   17
   11
   10
 + 11
```
d
```
   14
   12
   13
 + 10
```

8
a
```
   21
   13
   10
 + 14
```
b
```
   23
   11
   12
 + 13
```
c
```
   22
   10
   15
 + 11
```
d
```
   25
   11
   10
 + 12
```

9
a
```
   23
   21
   22
 + 11
```
b
```
   21
   20
   24
 + 12
```
c
```
   25
   21
   22
 + 10
```
d
```
   22
   21
   20
 + 14
```

10
a
```
   31
   22
   24
 + 22
```
b
```
   33
   20
   22
 + 23
```
c
```
   32
   34
   21
 + 12
```
d
```
   35
   30
   23
 + 11
```

11
a
```
   16
   15
   13
 + 11
```
b
```
   17
   12
   12
 + 13
```
c
```
   15
   13
   13
 + 14
```
d
```
   18
   11
   12
 + 14
```

12
a
```
   19
   13
   15
 + 12
```
b
```
   17
   14
   15
 + 12
```
c
```
   18
   15
   14
 + 11
```
d
```
   16
   15
   17
 + 10
```

13
a $15 + 13 + 17 + 11$
b $14 + 12 + 16 + 15$
c $16 + 14 + 14 + 13$
d $13 + 12 + 19 + 13$

14
a $18 + 13 + 22 + 24$
b $17 + 15 + 11 + 34$
c $13 + 27 + 11 + 26$
d $32 + 14 + 15 + 15$

15
a $17 + 18 + 12 + 14$
b $15 + 17 + 13 + 16$
c $13 + 14 + 18 + 16$
d $14 + 13 + 19 + 16$

16
a $27 + 28 + 14 + 13$
b $39 + 15 + 12 + 17$
c $32 + 14 + 19 + 17$
d $23 + 27 + 17 + 15$

17
a $16 + 29 + 28 + 19$
b $19 + 16 + 18 + 38$
c $37 + 19 + 17 + 18$
d $28 + 15 + 19 + 29$

18
a $37 + 28 + 19 + 15$
b $29 + 16 + 29 + 25$
c $19 + 27 + 28 + 24$
d $26 + 17 + 18 + 38$

19
a
```
   14
    3
   16
 +  2
```
b
```
   13
    6
   12
 +  5
```
c
```
    7
   14
   11
 +  4
```
d
```
    4
   18
   13
 +  1
```

20
a
```
   17
    4
   16
 +  2
```
b
```
   14
    7
   15
 +  3
```
c
```
    3
   13
   15
 +  7
```
d
```
    5
   18
   12
 +  4
```

21
a
```
   25
    7
   11
 +  4
```
b
```
   12
    8
   24
 +  3
```
c
```
    3
   11
   27
 +  6
```
d
```
    5
   25
   12
 +  6
```

22
a
```
   15
    6
    4
 +  2
```
b
```
   13
    8
    5
 +  2
```
c
```
    9
   11
    6
 +  1
```
d
```
    3
    8
   12
 +  4
```

23
a
```
   21
   16
   13
 +  6
```
b
```
   14
   22
    7
 + 12
```
c
```
   12
    9
   24
 + 10
```
d
```
    3
   11
   13
 + 28
```

24
a $11 + 8 + 13 + 9$
b $15 + 4 + 17 + 5$
c $9 + 15 + 14 + 4$
d $7 + 14 + 16 + 4$

25
a $24 + 7 + 18 + 5$
b $15 + 8 + 26 + 4$
c $6 + 28 + 16 + 3$
d $4 + 19 + 25 + 5$

26
a $32 + 6 + 19 + 8$
b $7 + 26 + 28 + 4$
c $11 + 8 + 37 + 9$
d $5 + 29 + 22 + 8$

27
a $35 + 3 + 26 + 8$
b $9 + 45 + 12 + 6$
c $29 + 7 + 33 + 4$
d $3 + 41 + 9 + 19$

28
a $42 + 9 + 27 + 8$
b $56 + 8 + 14 + 7$
c $4 + 58 + 17 + 7$
d $3 + 29 + 45 + 9$

29
a $37 + 9 + 18 + 9$
b $27 + 8 + 29 + 8$
c $29 + 6 + 28 + 9$
d $19 + 9 + 36 + 8$

30
a $27 + 8 + 17 + 9$
b $6 + 19 + 19 + 18$
c $19 + 9 + 28 + 5$
d $8 + 16 + 18 + 19$

Example 3

Add the following to find the 'odd answer out'.

a $201 + 73 + 429$
b $300 + 16 + 397$
c $199 + 187 + 317$

a		b		c	
	201		300		199
	73		16		187
+	429	+	397	+	317
	703		713		703

So **b** has the 'odd answer out' because its answer is 713.

Exercise 3.3

Add the following and find the 'odd answer out'.

1 a

		b		c	
	234		127		15
	116		47		256
+	28	+	205	+	107

2 a

		b		c	
	215		124		173
	43		231		64
+	174	+	77	+	205

3 a $167 + 45 + 352$
  b $241 + 187 + 36$
  c $154 + 82 + 328$

4 a $326 + 145 + 44$
  b $275 + 36 + 214$
  c $33 + 255 + 227$

5 a

		b		c	
	232		42		61
	20		251		43
+	72	+	31	+	230

6 a $46 + 213 + 36$
  b $230 + 39 + 27$
  c $64 + 209 + 23$

7 a $48 + 63 + 245$
  b $27 + 306 + 23$
  c $282 + 37 + 38$

8 a

		b		c	
	314		322		113
	223		125		133
+	241	+	321	+	532

9 a

		b		c	
	612		430		532
	121		323		342
+	244	+	234	+	113

10 a $224 + 523 + 131$
  b $635 + 112 + 132$
  c $353 + 104 + 422$

11 a $213 + 244 + 178$
  b $152 + 313 + 169$
  c $316 + 124 + 194$

12 a $155 + 424 + 147$
  b $263 + 225 + 238$
  c $324 + 153 + 248$

13 a $454 + 143 + 172$
  b $375 + 242 + 252$
  c $296 + 142 + 431$

14 a $338 + 413 + 234$
  b $527 + 243 + 115$
  c $213 + 216 + 456$

15 a $228 + 384 + 213$
  b $320 + 259 + 346$
  c $299 + 338 + 188$

16 a

		b		c	
	223		42		36
	18		217		24
	32		25		212
+	12	+	11	+	13

17 a $34 + 13 + 32 + 147$
  b $15 + 34 + 114 + 53$
  c $25 + 132 + 33 + 26$

18 a $275 + 41 + 16 + 52$
  b $57 + 240 + 34 + 43$
  c $63 + 24 + 245 + 42$

19 a $55 + 20 + 31 + 211$
  b $43 + 21 + 241 + 12$
  c $31 + 222 + 24 + 50$

20 a $260 + 113 + 32 + 52$
  b $14 + 151 + 231 + 62$
  c $173 + 12 + 30 + 242$

21 a $57 + 12 + 303 + 211$
  b $144 + 401 + 26 + 13$
  c $22 + 214 + 333 + 15$

22 a $274 + 25 + 12 + 443$
  b $83 + 16 + 532 + 123$
  c $350 + 328 + 53 + 24$

23 a $255 + 324 + 221 + 56$
  b $363 + 346 + 12 + 145$
  c $37 + 440 + 122 + 257$

24 a $245 + 231 + 102 + 254$
  b $113 + 156 + 341 + 222$
  c $127 + 230 + 251 + 124$

25 a $166 + 341 + 202 + 232$
  b $275 + 330 + 122 + 114$
  c $284 + 311 + 133 + 213$

Example 4

Find the sum of:

a 406, 23, 17, 181, 109

b eighty-four, six hundred, two hundred and twenty-two, nine

a		b	
	406		84
	23		600
	17		222
	181	+	9
+	109		915
	736		

Exercise 3.4

In each of the following questions find which list of numbers has a different sum from the other two.

1 **a** 352, 41, 24, 216, 323
    b 507, 263, 50, 21, 125
    c 240, 401, 208, 54, 63

2 **a** 305, 23, 51, 40, 203
    b 32, 300, 207, 10, 73
    c 42, 23, 31, 406, 110

3 **a** 105, 3, 94, 550, 123
    b 81, 344, 302, 134, 4
    c 6, 470, 200, 152, 37

4 **a** 365, 81, 4, 2, 260
    b 482, 180, 5, 1, 54
    c 7, 261, 90, 352, 2

5 **a** 115, 58, 42, 55, 3
    b 41, 36, 8, 122, 56
    c 52, 154, 33, 6, 28

6 **a** eighty-seven, four hundred and one, two hundred and ninety, four
    b three hundred and twenty-seven, ninety, five, three hundred and seventy
    c six, eighty-two, one hundred and ninety-four, five hundred

7 **a** fifty-six, forty-two, two hundred and thirty, seven
    b two hundred and four, six, fifty, seventy-five
    c nine, ninety-four, two hundred, forty-two

8 **a** five hundred and seventy, two hundred and forty-one, five, three
    b six, four hundred and eighty-one, three hundred and forty, two
    c six hundred and fifty, five, four, one hundred and sixty

9 **a** two hundred, four hundred and four, three hundred and thirty-eight, fifty
    b one hundred and eleven, two hundred and six, sixty-five, six hundred
    c thirty, five hundred and twenty, one hundred and four, three hundred and twenty-eight

10 **a** three hundred and five, ninety-nine, fifty, one hundred and sixty-seven
    b ninety, eighty-eight, two hundred and twenty-six, two hundred and seven
    c one hundred and eighteen, forty, seventy-five, three hundred and eighty-eight

Subtracting

Example 5

Subtract the following 'in your head' to find the 'odd answer out'.

a 26 − 12   **b** 88 − 74
c 50 − 36   **d** 43 − 28

This is one way to think the problems through:

a (20 − 10)   (6 − 2)
       10   +   4   = 14

b (80 − 70)   (8 − 4)
       10   +   4   = 14

c (50 − 30)   (0 − 6)
       20   −   6   = 14

d (40 − 20)   (3 − 8)
       20   −   5   = 15

So **d** has the 'odd answer out' because its answer is 15.

Exercise 3.5

Subtract the following to find the 'odd answer out'.

1 **a** 66 − 41   **b** 49 − 23   **c** 77 − 52   **d** 55 − 30

2 **a** 57 − 23   **b** 88 − 55   **c** 65 − 32   **d** 79 − 46

3 **a** 58 − 16
    b 84 − 41
    c 75 − 33
    d 97 − 55

4 **a** 97 − 43
    b 74 − 20
    c 89 − 35
    d 66 − 11

5 **a** 68 − 12
    b 97 − 51
    c 86 − 40
    d 79 − 33

6 **a** 96 − 33
    b 75 − 11
    c 87 − 24
    d 69 − 6

7 **a** 78 − 26
    b 94 − 43
    c 59 − 7
    d 66 − 14

8 **a** 96 − 51
    b 49 − 4
    c 75 − 40
    d 57 − 12

9 **a** 39 − 3
    b 67 − 31
    c 46 − 10
    d 98 − 52

10 **a** 79 − 35
    b 54 − 20
    c 86 − 52
    d 97 − 63

11 **a** 72 − 37
    b 94 − 59
    c 63 − 28
    d 81 − 45

12 a 75 − 28	**13 a** 44 − 28
b 91 − 44	**b** 63 − 46
c 63 − 15	**c** 71 − 55
d 86 − 39	**d** 55 − 39

12 a 75 − 28   **13 a** 44 − 28   **14 a** 62 − 34
  b 91 − 44   **b** 63 − 46   **b** 45 − 16
  c 63 − 15   **c** 71 − 55   **c** 86 − 57
  d 86 − 39   **d** 55 − 39   **d** 74 − 45

15 a 64 − 25   **16 a** 51 − 45   **17 a** 52 − 25
  b 87 − 49   **b** 93 − 87   **b** 83 − 57
  c 75 − 37   **c** 74 − 69   **c** 45 − 18
  d 90 − 52   **d** 80 − 74   **d** 96 − 69

18 a 62 − 13   **19 a** 93 − 37   **20 a** 62 − 24
  b 85 − 37   **b** 75 − 29   **b** 94 − 56
  c 73 − 25   **c** 62 − 16   **c** 97 − 49
  d 90 − 42   **d** 55 − 9   **d** 46 − 8

11 a 729 and 243   **12 a** 947 and 383
  b 857 and 381   **b** 826 and 262
  c 648 and 162   **c** 769 and 195

13 a 615 and 253   **14 a** 492 and 237
  b 538 and 186   **b** 664 and 419
  c 807 and 445   **c** 573 and 328

15 a 381 and 257   **16 a** 373 and 27
  b 550 and 426   **b** 361 and 16
  c 272 and 138   **c** 384 and 39

17 a 422 and 143   **18 a** 623 and 237
  b 614 and 325   **b** 861 and 485
  c 541 and 262   **c** 744 and 368

19 a 614 and 31   **20 a** 543 and 75
  b 638 and 54   **b** 505 and 38
  c 606 and 23   **c** 514 and 46

Example 6

Subtract to find the difference between the
following pairs of numbers and so find the 'odd
answer out'.

a 676 and 394   **b** 309 and 27
c 584 and 292

$$\begin{array}{r} \textbf{a}\quad 676 \\ -\ 394 \\ \hline 282 \end{array} \qquad \begin{array}{r} \textbf{b}\quad 309 \\ -\ 27 \\ \hline 282 \end{array} \qquad \begin{array}{r} \textbf{c}\quad 584 \\ -\ 292 \\ \hline 292 \end{array}$$

So **c** has the 'odd answer out' because its answer
is 292.

Example 7

By adding and subtracting, work out the
following.

a 76 + 82 − 69   **b** 9 − 253 + 607

a
$$\begin{array}{r} 76 \\ +\ 82 \\ \hline 158 \\ -\ 69 \\ \hline 89 \end{array}$$

b Rearrange as follows:
9 + 607 − 253

$$\begin{array}{r} 9 \\ +\ 607 \\ \hline 616 \end{array} \qquad \begin{array}{r} 616 \\ -\ 253 \\ \hline 363 \end{array}$$

Exercise 3.6

Subtract to find the difference between the following
pairs of numbers and so find the 'odd answer out'.

1 a 797 and 352   **2 a** 876 and 252
  b 856 and 421   **b** 968 and 344
  c 669 and 234   **c** 747 and 133

3 a 586 and 214   **4 a** 797 and 541
  b 794 and 432   **b** 376 and 130
  c 678 and 306   **c** 658 and 412

5 a 897 and 384   **6 a** 788 and 147
  b 759 and 236   **b** 996 and 354
  c 983 and 460   **c** 849 and 208

7 a 895 and 432   **8 a** 598 and 253
  b 668 and 205   **b** 976 and 621
  c 789 and 327   **c** 665 and 320

9 a 397 and 74   **10 a** 594 and 51
  b 365 and 52   **b** 579 and 37
  c 386 and 63   **c** 585 and 43

Exercise 3.7

Find the 'odd answer out' for the following:

1 a 288 + 154 − 317   **2 a** 38 + 307 − 182
  b 396 + 178 − 439   **b** 508 + 29 − 384
  c 197 + 186 − 258   **c** 19 + 425 − 291

3 a 382 + 275 − 39   **4 a** 87 + 555 − 176
  b 191 + 485 − 48   **b** 658 + 73 − 265
  c 272 + 363 − 17   **c** 57 + 893 − 494

5 a 7 + 348 − 78   **6 a** 25 − 41 + 58
  b 9 + 324 − 46   **b** 18 − 49 + 74
  c 6 + 368 − 87   **c** 36 − 53 + 59

7 a 134 − 196 + 225   **8 a** 57 − 148 + 235
  b 190 − 319 + 292   **b** 81 − 282 + 355
  c 248 − 262 + 167   **c** 72 − 109 + 191

9 a 8 − 29 + 135   **10 a** 58 − 76 + 181
  b 5 − 68 + 187   **b** 30 − 42 + 185
  c 7 − 80 + 197   **c** 19 − 47 + 191

Adding and subtracting

Example 8

In a competition, five balls are rolled into numbered slots. If four balls have been rolled as shown what is
a the total score,
b the score that the fifth ball must make to win
   (i) a 'free go',   (ii) a prize?

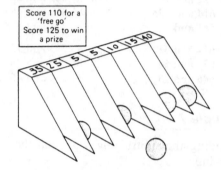

Score 110 for a 'free go'
Score 125 to win a prize

a Total score = 25 + 5 + 15 + 40 = 85
b (i) To win a 'free go' the fifth ball must score
     110 − 85 = 25
   (ii) To win a prize the fifth ball must score
     125 − 85 = 40

Exercise 3.8

1 The milkman uses a crate containing 20 bottles to deliver milk to Short Street.
How many bottles will he have left when he gets to the end of the street?

MILK ORDERS FOR SHORT STREET
MRS JONES, No.1 4 BOTTLES
MR ADAMS, No.2 2 BOTTLES
MRS BUTLER, No.3 1 BOTTLE
MISS HAYNES, No.4 NONE TODAY.
MRS ASHURST, No.5 3 BOTTLES
MR BIGGS, No.6 1 BOTTLE

2 Natalie arrived at the railway station 15 minutes before her train was due, but the train arrived 27 minutes late.
How many minutes did she have to wait?
How many minutes less than one hour did she have to wait?

3 A man bought a coffee and a slice of cake at the snack bar.
If he gave a £5 note, what change should he have received?

PRICE LIST	
COFFEE (cup)	50 p
TEA (cup)	50 p
CAKE (per slice)	85 p
SANDWICHES	90 p

4 A school relay team complete a 4 by 100 metres run in 51 seconds.
If the first, second and third runners complete their sprints in 12, 14 and 13 seconds respectively, what is the last runner's time?

5 A footballer scores an equalizing goal after 57 minutes. If the match is scheduled to last 90 minutes, how many minutes are left after he scores?
The match however ends as a draw, and 30 minutes of extra time are played.
How long after his goal does the match finally end?

6

WILLOW BANK SCHOOL
SPORTS DAY 16th JULY

FIRST EVENT   2.00 PM

TROPHY
PRESENTATION   5.00 PM

At Willow Bank School all competitors have to enter for their events at least 14 days before Sports Day.
What is the latest date for entries?
If Sports Day is 13 days before the end of the term, on what date does the school close for the summer holiday?

7 At Willow Bank School there are 455 girls and 428 boys.
How many pupils are there altogether?
How many more girls are there than boys?

8 My car has 23 litres of petrol in its tank. I use up 8 litres in driving to the seaside where I fill the tank up.
If the tank holds 32 litres, how many litres do I put in?

9 Peter and William compete in an archery contest. Look at their scores below.

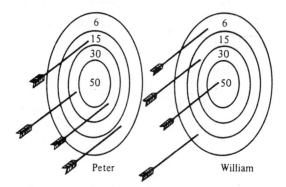

Who has won the contest and by how many points?

10 Which is the shorter way from Liverpool to Manchester and by how many kilometres?

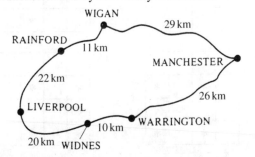

Magic squares

16	3	2	13
5	10	11	8
9	6	7	12
4	15	14	1

In a *magic square*, each number is different but the sum of each row, each column and each of the two diagonals is the same.
In the above example, check that each adds up to the same number, namely 34.

Exercise 3.9

State which of the following are *not* magic squares.

1

4	3	8
9	5	1
2	7	6

2

5	3	10
11	6	1
2	9	7

3

7	2	3
1	4	8
5	6	1

4

10	9	5
3	8	13
11	7	6

5

4	4	7
8	5	2
3	6	6

6

7	8	3
2	6	10
9	4	5

7

3	11	4
7	6	5
8	1	9

8

10	6	5
3	7	12
9	8	4

Exercise 3.10

Copy and complete each magic square by finding the missing numbers.

1

		6
	5	
4	3	

2

4	7	10
		8

3

9		4
	6	
		3

4

7	12	5
11		

5

	11		
	8	12	
4	5		16
15	10	6	

6

			6
8	15	3	12
7	16		
		14	9

7

6		11	9
17	4		
5			
10		7	13

8

10			11
	16	13	2
	4		
6		12	7

7

*	*		
*	*		

8

	*		
*		*	
	*		

9

	22	1	20	19
24	8		16	
	21	13		
14	10		18	12
7	4		6	23

10

8	25	18		4
7	11			
26	12	14	16	2
	19		17	23
24		10	13	

9

		*	
	*		*
		*	

10

*		*	
*		*	

11

		*	*
		*	*

12

	*		*
	*		*

13

*	*		
*	*		

14

		*	
	*		*
		*	

15

	*		*
	*		*

16

*		*	
*		*	

17

	*		
			*
*			
		*	

18

	*		
*		*	
	*		

Exercise 3.11

9	4	16	5
7	14	2	11
6	15	3	10
12	1	13	8

In the questions below, the stars represent numbers from the magic square above.
In each case find the sum of the four numbers.

1

	*	*	
	*	*	

2

		*	*
		*	*

19

		*	
*			
			*
	*		

20

		*	*
		*	*

3

*			*
*			*

4

	*	*	
	*	*	

5

*	*		
*	*		

6

		*	*
		*	*

Unit 4   Information in tables

Example 1

A saleswoman for a firm that makes crisps visited four different shops. The table below shows the number of wholesale boxes of crisps purchased by each shop.

variety	shop *A*	shop *B*	shop *C*	shop *D*
ready salted	11	5	3	6
salt and vinegar	5	2	1	2
cheese and onion	2	1	1	1
prawn cocktail	2	2	0	6

a How many boxes of prawn cocktail crisps were bought by Shop D?
b How many boxes of crisps were bought by Shop C?
c How many boxes of ready salted crisps were bought?
d Which shop bought the least number of boxes?
e How many boxes of crisps were bought altogether?

a 6   **b** 5 $(3 + 1 + 1 + 0)$ **c** 25 $(11 + 5 + 3 + 6)$

d Shop C (Shop A bought 20, Shop B bought 10, Shop C bought 5 and Shop D bought 15)

e 50 $(20 + 10 + 5 + 15)$

Exercise 4.1

1 The table below shows how many boys and girls there are in each of the five classes at High Lane School.

	Class 1	Class 2	Class 3	Class 4	Class 5
boys	11	8	10	9	12
girls	9	7	8	7	9

a How many boys are there in Class 4?
b How many girls are there altogether in classes 2, 3 and 4?
c One day, 45 boys and 36 girls in these five classes are present. How many boys and girls are absent?
d How many pupils are there in these five classes?

2 At West Hill School, the library books are classed as fiction, non-fiction or technical. The number of books borrowed by four pupils during a certain week are shown below.

	Jandeep	Peter	Michael	Tanya
fiction	1	0	0	2
non-fiction	2	0	1	1
technical	2	1	1	0

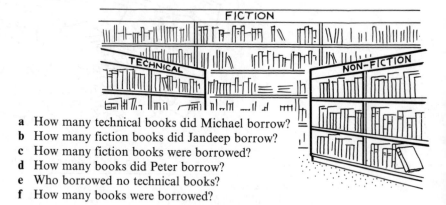

a How many technical books did Michael borrow?
b How many fiction books did Jandeep borrow?
c How many fiction books were borrowed?
d How many books did Peter borrow?
e Who borrowed no technical books?
f How many books were borrowed?

3 The table below shows the goals scored by four boys in the school football team in a three-round competition.

	Peter	William	Nathan	David
first round	2	1	1	1
semi-final	1	0	0	1
final	2	0	1	0

a How many goals did David score in the semi-final?
b Who scored 2 goals in the final?
c Who scored the least goals in the competition?
d How many goals were scored in the first round?
e How many goals did Nathan score?
f How many goals were scored altogether?

4 The table below shows how many coins four girls each have in their purses.

	Josie	Martha	Shellene	Sally
1p coins	4	2	2	1
2p coins	3	1	4	7
5p coins	2	1	2	3
10p coins	3	2	1	0

a How many 10p coins does Shellene have?
b Who has three 5p coins?
c How many coins does Sally have in her purse?
d What is the value of the coins in Josie's purse?
e Who has the least money in her purse?
f How much money altogether do the four girls have in their purses?

5 All long-distance trains from Newcastle station use platform 8, platform 9 or platform 10. The table shows the numbers of trains to the various destinations.

	London	Scotland	Birmingham	Liverpool
platform 8	4	4	5	2
platform 9	6	2	3	1
platform 10	6	4	1	3

a How many trains for Birmingham leave from platform 9?
b Which platform has only one train leaving for Liverpool?
c How many of the trains leave from platform 10?
d How many of the trains leave for Scotland?
e Which platform has the most long-distance trains leaving?
f How many long-distance trains leave Newcastle station?

6 The table below shows how many pupils from High Lane School had a school lunch on each day of a certain week.

	Class 1	Class 2	Class 3	Class 4	Class 5
Monday	12	5	8	6	11
Tuesday	9	7	7	8	9
Wednesday	11	7	7	11	14
Thursday	12	6	8	6	8
Friday	8	5	10	9	8

a How many pupils from Class 4 had lunch on Thursday?
b Which class had 5 pupils staying to lunch on Friday?
c How many lunches did Class 3 eat during the week?
d How many lunches were eaten on Tuesday?
e On which day of the week were the most lunches eaten?
f Which class ate the second highest number of lunches during the week?

7 A man sold ice lollies at a fair which was held for three days. The table below shows how many of each type of lolly he sold on each of the three days.

	orange	lemon	lime	raspberry
Thursday	50	30	20	25
Friday	40	25	15	30
Saturday	60	40	30	35

  a How many orange lollies did he sell on Thursday?
  b On which day did he sell the most raspberry lollies?
  c On which day was lemon the third most popular flavour?
  d How many lime lollies did he sell?
  e How many lollies did he sell on Friday?
  f The man took a stock of 120 raspberry lollies to the fair. How many did he have left?

8 At an airport there are three snack bars. The table below shows how many sandwiches each bar sold on a certain day.

	tuna	egg	cheese	tomato
waiting room bar	40	30	25	15
entrance hall bar	30	15	15	20
concourse bar	25	25	25	30

  a How many cheese sandwiches were sold by the concourse bar?
  b Which bar sold the least tomato sandwiches?
  c How many egg sandwiches were sold?
  d How many sandwiches were sold by the entrance hall bar?
  e Which bar sold the most sandwiches?
  f Which was the second most popular sandwich filling?

9 The table below shows how many pieces were left on the board at the end of a game of chess.

	pawns	castles	knights	bishops	kings	queens
black	4	1	0	2	1	1
white	6	1	2	0	1	0

  a How many black bishops were left on the board?
  b How many white pawns were left on the board?
  c How many knights were left on the board?
  d How many black pieces were left on the board?
  e How many pieces were left on the board?
  f Each player starts the game with 16 pieces.
     Which player lost the most pieces during the game?

10 The table below shows how many vehicles used a ferry on each day of an Easter holiday period.

	cars	vans	motorcycles
Friday	50	20	20
Saturday	40	15	15
Sunday	60	15	25
Monday	50	10	30
Tuesday	30	5	15

a How many vans used the ferry on Monday?
b On which day were the greatest number of motor cycles carried?
c On which day were the greatest number of vehicles carried?
d On which day were the least number of vehicles carried?
e How many cars were carried during the holiday?
f How many vehicles were carried during the holiday?

11 At West Hill School the pupils are given their examination results by being told that they have either a pass, a credit or a failure. The table below shows the results of four pupils.

	Kelly	Theo	Luke	Shona
passes	5	3	4	5
credits	1	4	1	3
failures	2	1	3	0

a Which pupil did not fail any exams?
b Which pupil gained the most credits?
c In how many subjects did the pupils take examinations?
d How many pass grades were obtained altogether?
e A pass is worth 3 points, a credit is worth 7 points and a failure is worth 0 points. How many points did Luke score?
f Which pupil scored the most points?

Time

The first bicycle was invented in 1801. In 1995 this was 1995 − 1801 = 194 years ago.

Exercise 4.2

How long ago did these events take place?

1 The Battle of Hastings, 1066
2 The Battle of Waterloo, 1815
3 The Great Fire of London, 1666
4 The Spanish Armada, 1588
5 The end of the Hundred Years War, 1453
6 The start of World War I, 1914
7 The Queen's Coronation, 1953
8 The first landing on the Moon, 1969
9 The Romans leaving Britain, 410
10 The building of Hadrian's Wall, 126

Example 2

John's father was born in 1957. How many years old is he in 1995?

(1995 − 1957) = 38. He is 38 years old.

John is aged 12 in 1995. In what year was he born?

(1995 − 12) = 1983. He was born in 1983.

Exercise 4.3

Find how many years old each of the following people is in 1995. Their year of birth is given.

1 1980	2 1976	3 1972	4 1966
5 1961	6 1955	7 1951	8 1944
9 1937	10 1932	11 1925	12 1917
13 1908	14 1904	15 1892	

When were each of the following members of a family born? Their age in 1995 is given.

16 Tom, 3 years.
17 Polly, 7 years.
18 Jodie, 9 years.
19 Daniel, 13 years.
20 Aunt Pam, 24 years.
21 Uncle Bob, 27 years.
22 Mum, 32 years.
23 Dad, 38 years.
24 Aunt Jane, 45 years.
25 Uncle Fred, 49 years.
26 Grannie, 63 years.
27 Grandad, 66 years.
28 Great-Uncle Robert, 75 years.
29 Great-Grannie, 87 years.
30 Great-Grandad, 91 years.

January						February				
S		7	14	21	28		4	11	18	25
M	1	8	15	22	29		5	12	19	26
T	2	9	16	23	30		6	13	20	27
W	3	10	17	24	31		7	14	21	28
T	4	11	18	25		1	8	15	22	29
F	5	12	19	26		2	9	16	23	
S	6	13	20	27		3	10	17	24	

Example 3

a How many days are there from January 15th to February 12th?

Days left in January = 31 − 15 = 16
Days in February   = 12

Therefore the number of days
= 16 + 12 = 28

b What date is 14 days before February 5th?

Days in February = 5
Days in January = 14 − 5 = 9

Therefore, date in January = 31 − 9 = 22nd

'30 days in September, April, June and November. All the rest have 31, except for February alone, which has 28 days clear, and 29 each leap year.'

Exercise 4.4

How many days are there from:

1 January 19th to February 15th
2 January 11th to February 26th
3 January 2nd to February 7th
4 January 9th to February 6th

5 March 8th to April 14th
6 January 25th to February 3rd
7 January 20th to February 17th
8 May 22nd to June 24th
9 January 30th to February 13th
10 January 31st to February 27th?

What is the date:

11 6 days before February 4th
12 15 days before February 11th
13 19 days before April 9th
14 16 days before February 2nd
15 23 days before June 8th
16 26 days before February 23rd
17 34 days before February 16th
18 38 days before February 21st
19 49 days before August 22nd
20 54 days before September 28th
21 8 days after January 26th
22 12 days after January 23rd
23 15 days after March 18th
24 25 days after January 11th
25 33 days after January 7th?

Example 4

How many days are there from March 20th to June 24th?

Days in March $= 31 - 20 = 11$
Days in April and May $= 30 + 31 = 61$
Days in June $= 24$

Therefore, the number of days $=$
$11 + 61 + 24 = 96$

Exercise 4.5

How many days are there from:

1 March 25th to June 8th
2 May 22nd to August 14th
3 October 26th to January 21st
4 July 18th to October 5th
5 April 15th to July 16th
6 September 17th to December 23rd
7 June 8th to September 4th
8 November 6th to February 15th
9 March 27th to July 3rd
10 August 23rd to December 10th
11 May 28th to September 25th
12 October 14th to February 6th
13 July 11th to November 18th

14 April 12th to August 24th
15 September 5th to January 6th
16 June 3rd to October 10th
17 May 9th to July 28th
18 October 13th to December 7th
19 July 19th to September 11th
20 April 16th to June 20th?

digital clock

These two clocks both show the same time.
It is five to eight or 7.55 p.m.
The digital clock shows 24-hour time: the time is
19.55h. The first two figures show the number of
hours past midnight; the last two figures show
the number of minutes past the hour.

Example 5

Write these times in 24-hour clock time.

a 10.30 a.m.   **b** 4.30 a.m.   **c** 10.15 p.m.

a 10.30 a.m. $= 10.30$h
b 4.30 a.m. $= 04.30$h
c 10.15 p.m. $= 22.15$h

Exercise 4.6

Write these times in 24-hour clock time.

1 11.30 a.m.	**2** 10.15 a.m.	**3** 9.20 a.m.
4 7.25 a.m.	**5** 8.45 a.m.	**6** 5.40 a.m.
7 2.10 a.m.	**8** 3.50 a.m.	**9** 1.55 a.m.
10 4.00 a.m.	**11** 6.05 a.m.	**12** 3.30 p.m.
13 2.15 p.m.	**14** 6.10 p.m.	**15** 4.25 p.m.
16 7.45 p.m.	**17** 5.35 p.m.	**18** 1.40 p.m.
19 8.20 p.m.	**20** 9.55 p.m.	**21** 7.00 p.m.
22 6.25 p.m.	**23** 3.05 p.m.	**24** 9.50 p.m.
25 8.00 p.m.	**26** 10.20 p.m.	**27** 11.15 p.m.
28 10.55 p.m.	**29** 11.35 p.m.	**30** 12.00 p.m.

Example 6

Write these times in 12-hour clock time.

a 01.15h   **b** 12.00h   **c** 23.55h

a 01.15h = 1.15 a.m.
b 12.00h = 12 noon
c 23.55h = 11.55 p.m.

Exercise 4.7

Write these times in 12-hour clock time.

1 11.15 h	**2** 10.20 h	**3** 09.10 h
4 08.30 h	**5** 04.25 h	**6** 02.45 h
7 03.40 h	**8** 01.50 h	**9** 05.35 h
10 07.00 h	**11** 00.30 h	**12** 14.30 h
13 16.10 h	**14** 17.15 h	**15** 18.45 h
16 13.50 h	**17** 15.40 h	**18** 16.35 h
19 19.05 h	**20** 20.15 h	**21** 21.20 h
22 23.00 h	**23** 22.30 h	**24** 22.05 h
25 23.25 h	**26** 23.50 h	**27** 20.55 h
28 21.45 h	**29** 19.40 h	**30** 18.05 h

When using 24-hour clock time, it is easy to find how long something has lasted, such as the length of a lesson or the time of a journey. Subtract the starting time from the finishing time. But remember that there are only 60 minutes in one hour.

Example 7

a A television play starts at 21.25 h and ends at 23.50h. How long does it last?

Time taken =
$$\begin{array}{r} 23.50 \\ -\ 21.25 \\ \hline 02.25 \end{array}$$

Therefore the time taken is
2 hours 25 minutes.

b The games lesson starts at 09.45h and ends at 10.40h. How long does it last?

Time taken =
$$\begin{array}{r} 10.40 \\ -\ 09.45 \\ \hline 00.55 \end{array}$$

Therefore the lesson lasts 55 minutes.

Exercise 4.8

How long is it from:

1 15.10 h to 15.45 h	**2** 10.20 h to 11.35 h
3 16.05 h to 18.35 h	**4** 07.15 h to 09.55 h
5 11.05 h to 11.30 h	**6** 10.05 h to 13.40 h
7 14.25 h to 19.50 h	**8** 09.15 h to 10.30 h
9 15.50 h to 16.30 h	**10** 08.45 h to 09.10 h?

11 A football match started at 15.15 h and the final whistle blew at 16.55 h.
How long did the match last?

12 A film show at a cinema starts at 14.30 h and ends at 16.45 h.
How long does it last?

13 A newspaper boy begins delivering at 06.10 h and finishes at 07.15 h.
How long does it take him to complete the round?

14 An aeroplane leaves London (Heathrow) Airport at 11.05 h and arrives at Manchester (Ringway) Airport at 11.50 h.
How long does the flight last?

15 A ship leaves Liverpool at 13.15 h and arrives at Douglas (Isle of Man) at 17.20 h.
How long does the voyage last?

16 At a school the mid-morning break starts at 10.50 h and ends at 11.10 h.
How long does the break last?

17 A ship leaves Dover at 14.40 h and arrives in Calais at 16.15 h.
How long does the voyage last?

18 One morning I arrived at a bus stop at 08.55 h, but no bus came until 09.20 h.
How long did I have to wait?

19 Find the time taken by the train from London to each station.

London (Paddington)	(depart)	15.10 h
Oxford	(arrive)	16.15 h
Banbury	(arrive)	16.40 h
Leamington Spa	(arrive)	17.10 h
Solihull	(arrive)	17.30 h
Birmingham	(arrive)	17.45 h

20 Find the time taken by the train from London to each station.

London (Liverpool Street)	(depart)	09.05 h
Bishop's Stortford	(arrive)	09.40 h
Audley End	(arrive)	09.55 h
Cambridge	(arrive)	10.15 h
Ely	(arrive)	10.35 h
King's Lynn	(arrive)	11.20 h

21 Bus timetable

Halesowen-Clent-Belbroughton				
From Halesowen				
Halesowen	08.10	11.05	15.15	17.45
Manor Way	08.15	11.10	15.20	17.50
St. Kenelm's Pass	08.25	11.20	15.30	18.00
Clent	08.30	11.25	15.35	18.05
Belbroughton	08.35	11.30	15.40	18.10
From Belbroughton				
Belbroughton	08.45	12.00	15.50	18.30
Clent	08.50	12.05	15.55	18.35
St. Kenelm's Pass	08.55	12.10	16.00	18.40
Manor Way	09.05	12.20	16.10	18.50
Halesowen	09.10	12.25	16.15	18.55

a When (in 12-hour time) does:
  (i) the first bus leave Halesowen for Belbroughton?
  (ii) the last bus leave Clent for Belbroughton?
  (iii) the first bus leave Clent for Halesowen?
  (iv) the last bus leave Belbroughton for Halesowen?

b A boy who lives near to Manor Way goes to a school in Belbroughton. His school starts at 09.00 h and finishes at 15.30 h.
  (i) At what time does he catch the bus to school?
  (ii) How long does his journey take?
  (iii) After he arrives in Belbroughton, how long is there before school starts?
  (iv) At what time does he catch the bus home?
  (v) How long is there after school before the bus leaves?

c A girl who lives in Halesowen goes to meet a friend in Clent at 11.30 h.
  (i) At what time does she catch the bus to Clent?
  (ii) How long does her journey take?
  (iii) How long will she wait in Clent before meeting her friend?
  (iv) If she has to be back in Halesowen for her tea at 17.00 h, at what time will she catch the bus home?
  (v) How much time does she have to see her friend?

22 Bus timetable

Wetherby-Harewood-Otley				
From Wetherby				
Wetherby	09.05	13.35	16.45	18.30
Collingham	09.10	13.40	16.50	18.35
Harewood	09.20	13.50	17.00	18.45
Arthington	09.30	14.00	17.10	18.55
Pool	09.35	14.05	17.15	19.00
Otley	09.45	14.15	17.25	19.10
From Otley				
Otley	08.10	12.40	15.50	17.20
Pool	08.20	12.50	16.00	17.30
Arthington	08.25	12.55	16.05	17.35
Harewood	08.35	13.05	16.15	17.45
Collingham	08.45	13.15	16.25	17.55
Wetherby	08.50	13.20	16.30	18.00

a When (in 12-hour time) does:
  (i) the first bus leave Harewood for Otley?
  (ii) the last bus leave Wetherby for Otley?
  (iii) the first bus leave Arthington for Wetherby?
  (iv) the last bus leave Pool for Wetherby?

b A girl who lives in Harewood has to go to a netball tournament in Otley which lasts from 14.30 h to 16.30 h.
  (i) At what time does she catch the bus to Otley?
  (ii) How long does her journey take?
  (iii) After arriving in Otley, how long does she have before the tournament starts?
  (iv) At what time does she catch the bus home?
  (v) How long is there after the tournament before the bus leaves?

c Two boys who live in Pool decide to go to a fair in Wetherby which opens at 14.00 h.
  (i) At what time will they catch the bus to Wetherby?
  (ii) How long does their journey take?
  (iii) How long will they have to wait in Wetherby for the fair to open?
  (iv) At what time will they catch the bus home if they stay as long as possible?
  (v) If they leave the fair 10 minutes before the bus departs, how long do they have at the fair?

Unit 5 Multiplying and dividing I

These are important number facts which are practised in this unit.

×	1	2	3	4	5	6	7	8	9	10
1	1	2	3	4	5	6	7	8	9	10
2	2	4	6	8	10	12	14	16	18	20
3	3	6	9	12	15					30
4	4	8	12	16	20					40
5	5	10	15	20	25	30	35	40	45	50
6	6	12			30					60
7	7	14			35					70
8	8	16			40					80
9	9	18			45					90
10	10	20	30	40	50	60	70	80	90	100

Multiplying

Example 1

Multiply to find the 'odd answer out':

a 6×5 **b** 10×3 **c** 12×2

a 30   **b** 30   **c** 24

So **c** is the 'odd answer out' because its answer is 24.

Exercise 5.1

Multiply the following to find the 'odd answer out'.

	a	**b**	**c**
1	2×6	4×3	5×2
2	3×5	3×4	6×2
3	4×4	8×2	5×5
4	5×6	2×9	3×10
5	5×4	10×2	9×2
6	5×8	4×10	7×5
7	3×5	4×5	2×10
8	6×5	10×3	$2 \times 2 \times 3$
9	8×10	$3 \times 3 \times 10$	$4 \times 2 \times 10$
10	$2 \times 2 \times 10$	6×5	$2 \times 3 \times 5$

Example 2

Multiply to find the 'odd answer out':

a 26×5 **b** 13×10 **c** 25×6

```
a    26        b    13        c    25
    ×5            ×10            ×6
    ───           ───            ───
    130           130            150
```

So **c** is the 'odd answer out' because its answer is 150.

Exercise 5.2

Multiply the following to find the 'odd answer out'.

	a	**b**	**c**
1	12×6	14×3	21×2
2	13×5	12×4	16×3
3	14×4	27×2	28×2
4	19×5	10×12	15×8
5	8×15	6×20	27×5
6	23×5	24×5	40×3
7	26×5	30×3	65×2
8	28×10	63×5	105×3
9	25×8	19×10	40×5
10	55×5	27×10	54×5

Example 3

Find the product of:

a 26×25 **b** 93×52

You can use a calculator or you can find the products like this:

```
a     26                         b     93
     ×25                              ×52
     ───                              ───
     520   (26 × 20)                 4650   (93 × 50)
     130   (26 × 5)                   186   (93 × 2)
     ───                              ────
     650   (26 × 25)                 4836   (93 × 52)
```

Exercise 5.3

1	27×25	2	34×43
3	24×51	4	42×14
5	88×55	6	97×21
7	65×12	8	76×15
9	64×55	10	89×22
11	53×35	12	42×24
13	51×15	14	52×25
15	54×25	16	54×43
17	79×52	18	68×21
19	89×25	20	99×55

Example 4

A gardener plants 53 rows of trees with 244 trees in each row. How many trees does she plant altogether?

Number of trees planted $= 244 \times 53$

```
     244
      53
  12 200   (244 × 50)
     732   (244 × 3)
  12 932   (244 × 53)
```

Exercise 5.4

1 A milkman uses crates which hold 6 rows of 5 bottles each.
How many bottles are there in 155 crates?

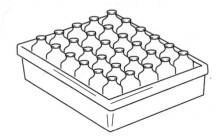

2 A shop buys pencils in boxes of 144.
How many pencils are there in 25 boxes?

3 A farmer sells eggs in trays with 12 rows of 12 eggs.
How many eggs are there in 33 trays?

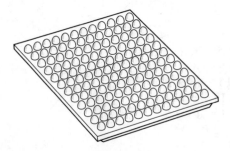

4 There are 15 players in a rugby team. Sixty-four rugby teams enter the first round of a cup competition.
How many players take part in the first round of the cup competition?

5 A bottle of lemonade holds 330 millilitres.
How much liquid does it take to fill 25 bottles?

6 A can of rice pudding holds 425 grams.
How much rice pudding is there in a box of 45 cans?

7 There are 365 days in a year. Mark is celebrating his 45th birthday today.
How many days has he lived? (Ignore leap years.)

8 A rabbit has 15 daughters, each of which has 15 daughters, each of which has 15 daughters, each of which has 15 daughters.
How many great-great-granddaughters does the original rabbit have?

9 A computer fanatic has 189 games in his collection, each of which cost £25.
How much did the collection cost altogether?

10 A skyscraper has 99 floors, each with 125 offices.
How many offices are there in the skyscraper?

Dividing

Example 5

Using division, find the 'odd answer out'.

a $45 \div 5$ **b** $8 \div 1$ **c** $18 \div 2$

a 9   **b** 8   **c** 9

So **b** is the 'odd answer out' because its answer is 8.

Exercise 5.5

Using division, find the 'odd answer out'.

	a	**b**	**c**
1	$12 \div 2$	$12 \div 3$	$20 \div 5$
2	$45 \div 9$	$36 \div 9$	$50 \div 10$
3	$12 \div 4$	$20 \div 5$	$40 \div 10$
4	$14 \div 2$	$40 \div 5$	$16 \div 2$
5	$18 \div 2$	$9 \div 1$	$70 \div 7$
6	$80 \div 8$	$70 \div 10$	$7 \div 1$
7	$50 \div 5$	$30 \div 6$	$20 \div 2$
8	$9 \div 3$	$15 \div 5$	$16 \div 4$
9	$14 \div 7$	$6 \div 2$	$18 \div 9$
10	$100 \div 10$	$40 \div 8$	$30 \div 3$

Example 6

Using division, find the 'odd answer out'.

a $440 \div 8$ **b** $216 \div 4$ **c** $165 \div 3$

a
$$\begin{array}{r} 55 \\ 8\overline{)440} \\ \underline{40} \quad (8 \times 5) \\ 40 \\ \underline{40} \quad (8 \times 5) \end{array}$$

b
$$\begin{array}{r} 54 \\ 4\overline{)216} \\ \underline{20} \quad (4 \times 5) \\ 16 \\ \underline{16} \quad (4 \times 4) \end{array}$$

a
$$\begin{array}{r} 55 \\ 3\overline{)165} \\ \underline{15} \quad (3 \times 5) \\ 15 \\ \underline{15} \quad (3 \times 5) \end{array}$$

So **b** is the 'odd answer out' because its answer is 54.

Exercise 5.6

Using division, find the 'odd answer out'.

	a	**b**	**c**
1	$75 \div 3$	$96 \div 4$	$200 \div 8$
2	$410 \div 5$	$164 \div 2$	$810 \div 10$
3	$1800 \div 8$	$672 \div 3$	$900 \div 4$
4	$3072 \div 6$	$2052 \div 4$	$2560 \div 5$
5	$1065 \div 5$	$1272 \div 6$	$1484 \div 7$
6	$168 \div 2$	$410 \div 5$	$420 \div 5$
7	$1414 \div 7$	$812 \div 4$	$1818 \div 9$
8	$3006 \div 6$	$3514 \div 7$	$4016 \div 8$
9	$1750 \div 7$	$2040 \div 8$	$2295 \div 9$
10	$1012 \div 4$	$1512 \div 6$	$1764 \div 7$

Example 7

Using division, find the 'odd answer out'.

a $442 \div 8$ **b** $217 \div 4$ **c** $167 \div 3$

a
$$\begin{array}{r} 55 \quad \text{remainder 2} \\ 8\overline{)442} \\ \underline{40} \quad (8 \times 5) \\ 42 \\ \underline{40} \quad (8 \times 5) \\ 2 \end{array}$$

b
$$\begin{array}{r} 54 \quad \text{remainder 1} \\ 8\overline{)217} \\ \underline{20} \quad (4 \times 5) \\ 17 \\ \underline{16} \quad (4 \times 4) \\ 1 \end{array}$$

c
$$\begin{array}{r} 55 \quad \text{remainder 2} \\ 3\overline{)167} \\ \underline{15} \quad (3 \times 5) \\ 17 \\ \underline{15} \quad (3 \times 5) \\ 2 \end{array}$$

So **b** is the 'odd answer out' because its answer is 54 remainder 1.

We can also work out remainders with a calculator.

Example 8

With a calculator, find the 'odd answer out'.

a $442 \div 8$ **b** $217 \div 4$ **c** $167 \div 3$

a $442 \div 8 = 55.25$

$8 \times 55 = 440$

$442 - 440 = 2$

So $442 \div 8 = 55$ remainder 2

b $217 \div 4 = 54.25$

$4 \times 54 = 216$

$217 - 216 = 1$

So $217 \div 4 = 54$ remainder 1

c $167 \div 3 = 55.666\,667$

$3 \times 55 = 165$

$167 - 165 = 2$

So $167 \div 3 = 55$ remainder 2

So **b** is the 'odd answer out' because its answer is 54 remainder 1.

Exercise 5.7

Find the 'odd answer out'.

	a		b		c	
1	a	$1352 \div 6$	b	$1577 \div 7$	c	$674 \div 3$
2	a	$4100 \div 8$	b	$1027 \div 2$	c	$2564 \div 5$
3	a	$418 \div 5$	b	$169 \div 2$	c	$421 \div 5$
4	a	$4552 \div 9$	b	$2018 \div 4$	c	$1514 \div 3$
5	a	$859 \div 7$	b	$981 \div 8$	c	$619 \div 5$
6	a	$2262 \div 9$	b	$1767 \div 7$	c	$2011 \div 8$
7	a	$3335 \div 6$	b	$3869 \div 7$	c	$4421 \div 8$
8	a	$1938 \div 9$	b	$1723 \div 8$	c	$1294 \div 6$
9	a	$1754 \div 7$	b	$1254 \div 5$	c	$2005 \div 8$
10	a	$2563 \div 5$	b	$4612 \div 9$	c	$3075 \div 6$

Multiplying and dividing

Example 9

A baker has made 226 bread rolls.
How many bags of 6 rolls can she make up and how many rolls will be left over?

$226 \div 6 = 37.666\,667$

$6 \times 37 = 222$

$226 - 222 = 4$

So the baker can make up 37 bags with 4 rolls left over.

Exercise 5.8

1 A club needs to transport 69 people in four-seater cars.
How many cars will they need and how many empty seats will there be in the cars?

2 In a spare parts store, switches used to be stored in trays which each held 32 switches. There were 25 full trays of switches on the day they were reorganized into trays which each held 15 switches.
How many full trays of 15 switches were filled and how many switches were left over?

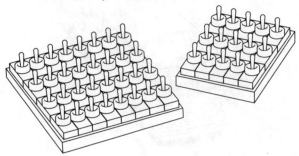

3 A farmer has an orchard of 212 trees, each of which produced an average of 515 apples.
If the apples are stored in trays of 55 apples, how many trays are filled and how many apples are left over?

4 A lottery win of £104 000 is shared by a syndicate of 25 people.
How much in total did a family of 4 people, who each had a place in the syndicate, receive?

5 After working for 34 days, a house painter is paid £1802.
   a How much was she paid for each day?
   b How much would she receive if she worked for 52 days at the same rate?

6 A book of raffle tickets contains 250 tickets.
   a How many tickets does Bob have if he has 8 full books and a partly used book with 123 tickets?
   b If Sherene has 1779 tickets, how many full books does she have and how many tickets in a partly used book?

7 A shop buys baked beans in boxes with 2 layers of cans, with 5 rows of 6 cans in each layer.
   a How many cans are there in 5 full boxes and a partly used box of 42 cans?
   b The shop has 617 cans of beans in stock. How many full boxes is this and how many cans in a partly used box?

8 A holiday for 45 school pupils will cost a total of £5625.
   a How much will each pupil pay?
   b How much would the same holiday cost in total if 68 pupils took part?

9 A teacher can claim 18p per mile travelling expenses.
   a If she goes to a meeting in a town 25 miles away, how much can she claim in travelling expenses?
   b If she claimed £38.16 in travelling expenses in one month, how many miles did she travel?

10 How long will the medicine in each of these bottles last?

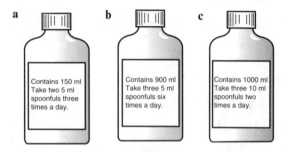

a Contains 150 ml
Take two 5 ml spoonfuls three times a day.

b Contains 900 ml
Take three 5 ml spoonfuls six times a day.

c Contains 1000 ml
Take three 10 ml spoonfuls two times a day.

11 Jeff is a handyman who still likes to work in feet and inches.
He has designed this airing cupboard shelf.

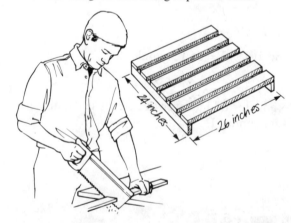

At the DIY shop, Jeff finds that the wood he needs is only available cut into these lengths:

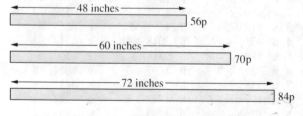

48 inches 56p

60 inches 70p

72 inches 84p

Find the least possible cost of building Jeff's shelf.

12 Find the least cost of building each of these shelves. Use the lengths of wood from the DIY shop in question **11**.

a

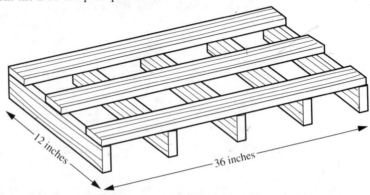

12 inches

36 inches

b

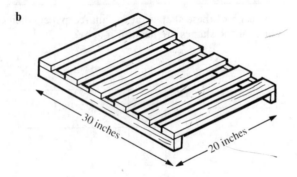

30 inches

20 inches

c

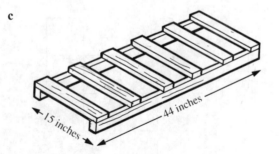

15 inches

44 inches

Unit 6 Nets

A *net* is a shape which folds to make a hollow solid.

This shape is the net for a cube.

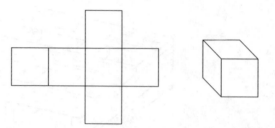

Exercise 6.1

Copy each of these shapes on to squared paper, then cut them out and fold them. Which of the shapes are nets for a cube?

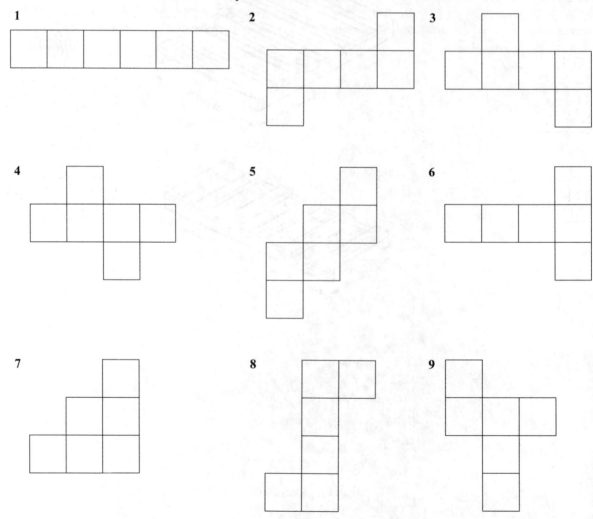

Exercise 6.2

This is the net (without glue flaps) for a box designed to hold 12 stock cubes.

1 How big are the stock cubes?

2 On squared paper, draw nets for two different shaped boxes which could hold 12 stock cubes each.

3 On squared paper, draw nets for two different shaped boxes which could hold 16 stock cubes each.

Exercise 6.3

This is the net for a regular tetrahedron (triangular-based pyramid).

This net is most easily drawn on triangular or *isometric* graph paper.

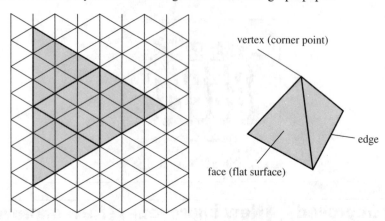

1 Use isometric graph paper to make a regular tetrahedron with edges 6 cm long. You will need to add glue flaps to the net so that you can assemble it.
2 How many faces does the tetrahedron have?
3 How many vertices does the tetrahedron have?
4 How many edges does the tetrahedron have?

Exercise 6.4

This is the net for a regular octahedron.

This net is most easily drawn on triangular or *isometric* graph paper.

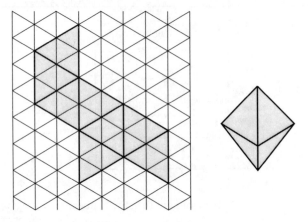

1 Use isometric graph paper to make a regular octahedron with edges 6 cm long. You will need to add glue flaps to the net so that you can assemble it.
2 How many faces does the octahedron have?
3 How many vertices does the octahedron have?
4 How many edges does the octahedron have?

Exercise 6.5

This is the net for a triangular prism.

This net is most easily drawn on triangular or *isometric* graph paper.

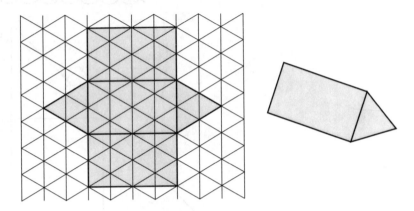

1 Use isometric graph paper to make a triangular prism with rectangular faces 4 cm high and 10 cm long. You will need to add glue flaps to the net so that you can assemble it.

2 How many faces does the triangular prism have?

3 How many vertices does the triangular prism have?

4 How many edges does the triangular prism have?

Exercise 6.6

The puzzle cube is made by fitting together three pyramids.
This is how to make a puzzle cube. The diagrams are shown half size. Copy them full size on to squared paper.

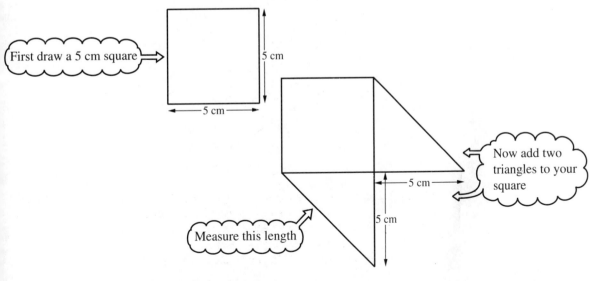

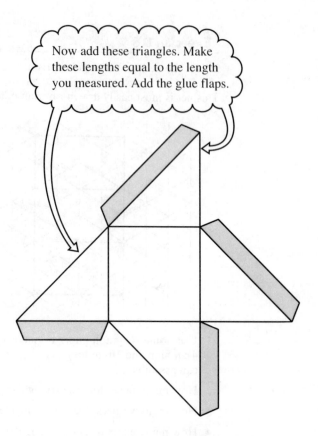

Now add these triangles. Make these lengths equal to the length you measured. Add the glue flaps.

Your net will assemble into a square pyramid which leans to one side.
Make three of these pyramids or work with two friends and make one pyramid each.
Three pyramids fit together to make the puzzle cube.
Experiment with your pyramids until you can fit them together easily.

Unit 7   Number patterns

Sequences

An *even* number can be divided exactly by 2. The sequence of even numbers starts:
2, 4, 6, 8, ...
An *odd* number has a remainder of 1 when divided by 2. The sequence of odd numbers starts: 1, 3, 5, 7, ...

Exercise 7.1

1 Six children have each thrown two dice. Look at their scores below.

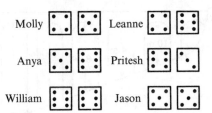

   a Whose scores are even numbers?
   b Whose scores are odd numbers?

2 List the next five even numbers starting from:
   a 4   **b** 16   **c** 32   **d** 88   **e** 100

3 List the next five odd numbers starting from:
   a 5   **b** 13   **c** 31   **d** 69   **e** 117

A *square* number is any number that can be represented by counters arranged in a square.

Example 1

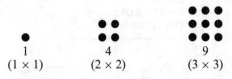

1   4   9
(1 × 1)   (2 × 2)   (3 × 3)

A square number is found by multiplying any number by itself.

A *rectangular* number is any number that can be represented by counters arranged in a rectangle.

Example 2

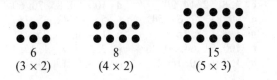

6   8   15
(3 × 2)   (4 × 2)   (5 × 3)

A *triangular* number is any number that can be represented by counters arranged in a triangle.

Example 3

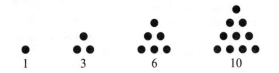

1   3   6   10

Exercise 7.2

1 Look at the numbers on the signposts A, B and C.

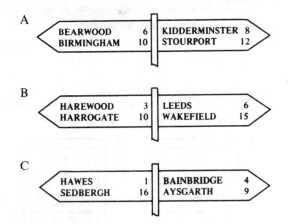

   a On which signpost are *all* the numbers square?
   b On which signpost are *all* the numbers rectangular?
   c On which signpost are *all* the numbers triangular?

2 State whether the following numbers are square (S), rectangular (R), triangular (T) or none of these (N). For example, 15 is (R,T); 17 is (N).
   a 12   **b** 14   **c** 16   **d** 21   **e** 7
   f 18   **g** 19   **h** 25   **i** 28   **j** 36

3 Can you find:
   a any odd numbers which are also square numbers?
   b any numbers which are both rectangular and odd?
   c any even numbers which are not rectangular? Give examples if you can.

4 Find the sum of:
   a the first three odd numbers
   b the first four odd numbers
   c the first five odd numbers
   d the first ten odd numbers
   e the first hundred odd numbers.

5 Make a list of the first six triangular numbers.
Add together:
a the first and second
b the second and third
c the third and fourth
d the fourth and fifth
e the fifth and sixth.
f The numbers in the above answers are all of
the same kind. What are they?

A *prime* number is one that cannot be divided by
any number apart from 1 and itself.

Example 4

The first five prime numbers are 2, 3, 5, 7 and
11.

Exercise 7.3

1 Look at the four buses **A**, **B**, **C** and **D**.

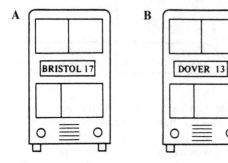

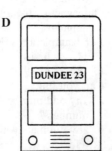

One of the buses is not displaying a prime
number. Which one is it?
2 List all the prime numbers between 1 and 30.
3 Which of the following are prime numbers?
   a 31   **b** 33   **c** 37   **d** 35   **e** 49   **f** 43
   g 51   **h** 41   **i** 53   **j** 57   **k** 63   **l** 61

A *sequence* is a set of numbers such that each
number is related to the next in the same way.

Example 5

a 1, 4, 7, 10, ... is a sequence in which each term
is three more than the one before it.
b 1, 4, 16, 64, ... is a sequence in which each
term is four times the one before it.

Exercise 7.4

1 Find the heights of the next two arches of the
viaduct below.

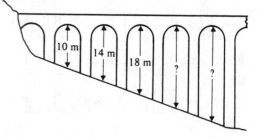

2 Find the next five terms of the sequences and
state the rule in each case.
   a 2, 4, 6, 8, ...   **b** 3, 6, 9, 12, ...
   c 12, 24, 36, 48, ...   **d** 50, 45, 40, 35, ...
   e 66, 60, 54, 48, ...   **f** 56, 49, 42, 35, ...
   g 8, 13, 18, 23, ...   **h** 5, 11, 17, 23, ...
   i 40, 36, 32, 28, ...   **j** 90, 82, 74, 66, ...

3 What is the distance to Stratford if the number is
the next one in the sequence?

HAGLEY	1
CLENT	3
BROMSGROVE	9
STRATFORD	?

4 Find the next three terms of the sequences and
state the rule in each case.
   a 1, 2, 4, 8, ...   **b** 1, 4, 16, 64, ...
   c 2, 20, 200, ...   **d** 32, 16, 8, ...
   e 243, 81, 27, ...   **f** 3125, 625, 125, ...

5 In each of the following, state which term is the
odd one out.
   a 2, 4, 6, 9, 10   **b** 3, 5, 7, 9, 10
   c 4, 8, 12, 14, 20   **d** 100, 90, 85, 70, 60
   e 90, 81, 72, 64, 54   **f** 55, 49, 42, 35, 28
   g 1, 3, 4, 8, 16   **h** 1, 4, 6, 16, 25
   i 100, 81, 64, 50, 36   **j** 2, 3, 5, 7, 11, 15, 17
   k 1, 3, 6, 10, 16, 21   **l** 6, 8, 9, 12, 14, 15

Multiples and factors

$1 \times 4 = 4$ $4 \times 4 = 16$
$2 \times 4 = 8$ $5 \times 4 = 20$
$3 \times 4 = 12$ $6 \times 4 = 24$

$4, 8, 12, 16, 20, 24, 28, 32, \ldots$ are all *multiples* of 4.

Example 6

List the first four multiples of 8.

$1 \times 8 = 8$ $3 \times 8 = 24$
$2 \times 8 = 16$ $4 \times 8 = 32$

So the first four multiples of 8 are 8, 16, 24, 32.

Exercise 7.5

List the first four multiples of:

1 2	**2** 5	**3** 3	**4** 6	**5** 10
6 7	**7** 9	**8** 11	**9** 12	**10** 20
11 50	**12** 40	**13** 60	**14** 25	**15** 15

Example 7

14, 28, 49, 64, 70

Which one of these numbers is *not* a multiple of 7?

$14 \div 7 = 2$ $49 \div 7 = 7$
$28 \div 7 = 4$ $64 \div 7 = 9 \text{ r} 1$
          $70 \div 7 = 10$

So 64 is not a multiple of 7.

Exercise 7.6

1 9, 13, 18, 21, 27.
   Which one of these numbers is not a multiple of 3?

2 30, 36, 40, 48, 54.
   Which one of these numbers is not a multiple of 6?

3 40, 48, 56, 62, 80.
   Which one of these numbers is not a multiple of 8?

4 20, 28, 32, 38, 44.
   Which one of these numbers is not a multiple of 4?

5 45, 54, 63, 74, 81.
   Which one of these numbers is not a multiple of 9?

6 66, 88, 99, 112, 121.
   Which one of these numbers is not a multiple of 11?

7 34, 48, 60, 72, 96.
   Which one of these numbers is not a multiple of 12?

8 80, 100, 120, 140, 150.
   Which one of these numbers is not a multiple of 20?

9 30, 45, 60, 70, 90.
   Which one of these numbers is not a multiple of 15?

10 100, 125, 150, 185, 200.
   Which one of these numbers is not a multiple of 25?

$6, 12, \underline{18}, 24, 30, \underline{36}, \ldots$ these are multiples of 6.

$9, \underline{18}, 27, \underline{36}, 45, 54, \ldots$ these are multiples of 9.

Notice that 18 and 36 are in both sets of multiples: they are common multiples of 6 and 9. The smallest of the common multiples is special: it is the LCM or *lowest common multiple*. 18 is the LCM of 6 and 9.

Example 8

Find the LCM of 12 and 15.

$1 \times 12 = 12$ $1 \times 15 = 15$
$2 \times 12 = 24$ $2 \times 15 = 30$
$3 \times 12 = 36$ $3 \times 15 = 45$
$4 \times 12 = 48$ $4 \times 15 = \underline{60}$
$5 \times 12 = \underline{60}$

So 60 is the LCM of 12 and 15.

Exercise 7.7

Find the LCM of:

1 3 and 4	**2** 5 and 6	**3** 9 and 10
4 4 and 5	**5** 5 and 8	**6** 3 and 5
7 4 and 8	**8** 3 and 12	**9** 2 and 6
10 5 and 10	**11** 4 and 12	**12** 6 and 10
13 4 and 6	**14** 6 and 8	**15** 6 and 9
16 9 and 12	**17** 9 and 15	**18** 10 and 15
19 8 and 12	**20** 12 and 20	**21** 2, 3 and 5
22 3, 4 and 9	**23** 2, 4 and 6	**24** 2, 4 and 10
25 3, 6 and 10		

The number 12 is a multiple of 1, 2, 3, 4, 6, and 12. These numbers are called the *factors* of 12.

Example 9

Find all the factors of 24.

$24 \div 1 = 24;$	so 1 and 24 are factors because $1 \times 24 = 24$.
$24 \div 2 = 12;$	so 2 and 12 are factors because $2 \times 12 = 24$.
$24 \div 3 = 8;$	so 3 and 8 are factors because $3 \times 8 = 24$.
$24 \div 4 = 6;$	so 4 and 6 are factors because $4 \times 6 = 24$.
$24 \div 5 = 4 \text{ r } 4$	so 5 is *not* a factor.
$24 \div 6 = 4;$	so 6 and 4 are factors, but these have already been found.

Therefore all the factors have now been found. All the factors of 24 are 1, 2, 3, 4, 6, 8, 12, and 24.

Exercise 7.8

Find all the factors of:

1	18	**2**	20	**3**	12	**4**	10	**5**	8
6	14	**7**	22	**8**	15	**9**	21	**10**	27
11	35	**12**	26	**13**	28	**14**	32	**15**	30
16	40	**17**	36	**18**	9	**19**	25	**20**	16

1, 2, 3, 6, 9, 18. These are all the factors of 18.
1, 2, 3, 5, 6, 10, 15, 30. These are all the factors of 30.
Notice that 1, 2, 3, and 6 are in both sets of factors: they are common factors of 18 and 30. The largest of the common factors is special: it is the HCF or *highest common factor*. 6 is the HCF of 18 and 30.

Example 10

Find the HCF of 28 and 42.

$28 \div 1 = 28$	$42 \div 1 = 42$
$28 \div 2 = 14$	$42 \div 2 = 21$
$28 \div 4 = 7$	$42 \div 3 = 14$
	$42 \div 6 = 7$

1, 2, 4, 7, 14, 28 are the factors of 28.
1, 2, 3, 6, 7, 14, 21, 42 are the factors of 42.
So the HCF of 28 and 42 is 14.

Exercise 7.9

Find the HCF of:

1	24 and 32	**2**	36 and 48
3	27 and 36	**4**	30 and 36
5	36 and 60	**6**	40 and 64
7	30 and 42	**8**	48 and 60
9	24 and 42	**10**	48 and 56
11	45 and 72	**12**	32 and 48
13	30 and 45	**14**	40 and 60
15	48 and 80	**16**	36 and 54
17	42 and 56	**18**	60 and 75
19	48 and 72	**20**	42 and 63
21	12, 24 and 30	**22**	36, 54 and 63
23	32, 48 and 72	**24**	54, 72 and 90
25	15, 45 and 60		

Two special factors of 10 are 2 and 5 because they are both prime numbers and their product is 10.
2 and 5 are called the *prime factors* of 10.
The prime numbers which are factors of 12 are 2 and 3. But the prime factors of 12 are $2 \times 2 \times 3$ because these are the prime numbers whose product is 12.

Example 11

Find the prime factors of:

a 42   **b** 100

a
$$\begin{array}{r} 2)\overline{42} \\ 3)\overline{21} \\ 7)\overline{7} \\ \overline{1} \end{array}$$

The prime factors of 42 are $2 \times 3 \times 7$

b
$$\begin{array}{r} 2)\overline{100} \\ 2)\overline{50} \\ 5)\overline{25} \\ 5)\overline{5} \\ \overline{1} \end{array}$$

The prime factors of 100 are $2 \times 2 \times 5 \times 5$

Exercise 7.10

Find the prime factors of:

1	30	**2**	66	**3**	70	**4**	78
5	110	**6**	130	**7**	154	**8**	210
9	84	**10**	140	**11**	132	**12**	88
13	104	**14**	56	**15**	40	**16**	120
17	72	**18**	168	**19**	80	**20**	48
21	112	**22**	180	**23**	108	**24**	162

Exercise 7.11

Find the 'odd answer out' for the following.

1   a   HCF of 12 and 15
    b   The second square number
    c   The second triangular number

2   a   The first square number
    b   The lowest prime number
    c   The first triangular number

3   a   HCF of 12 and 16
    b   LCM of 2 and 6
    c   LCM of 3 and 6

4   a   LCM of 2 and 3
    b   HCF of 16 and 24
    c   The third triangular number

5   a   LCM of 4 and 8
    b   HCF of 24 and 40
    c   The third square number

6   a   HCF of 24 and 60
    b   LCM of 3 and 4
    c   The fourth triangular number

7   a   The fifth triangular number
    b   The fourth square number
    c   HCF of 32 and 80

8   a   LCM of 6 and 9
    b   HCF of 36 and 54
    c   The sixth triangular number

9   a   LCM of 8 and 12
    b   The fifth square number
    c   HCF of 48 and 72

10   a   LCM of 4 and 6
     b   HCF of 36 and 60
     c   HCF of 16 and 48

Arrow graphs

A cat has three kittens: Pip, Tip and Nip.

Ma   Pip   Tip   Nip

Ma is the mother of Pip: Ma ⌒ Pip
where the arrow stands for 'is the mother of'.
The completed diagram is called an *arrow graph*.

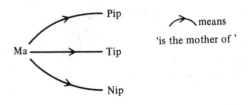

⌒ means 'is the mother of'

Example 12

Copy and complete the arrow graph where ⌒
means 'is three more than'.

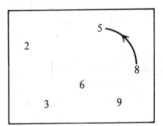

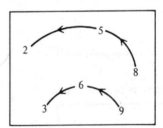

Exercise 7.12

Copy and complete each arrow graph.

1   ⌒ means 'is 2 more than'.

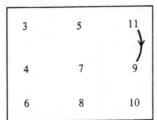

2 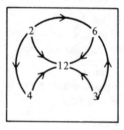 means 'is 4 more than'.

2	6	10
12	18	14
16	20	24

3 means 'is 4 less than'.

16	13	9
12	0	5
8	4	1

4 means 'is 6 less than'.

24	6	0
18	12	10
28	22	16

5 means 'is twice as much as'.

3	7	14
6	48	28
12	24	56

6 means 'is three times as much as'.

9	3	1
27	54	2
81	18	6

7 means 'is half as much as'.

64	32	48
8	16	24
4	6	12

8 means 'is a quarter as much as'.

64	16	4
32	$\frac{1}{4}$	1
8	2	$\frac{1}{2}$

Example 13

Find what the arrow means in the arrow graph.

The arrow means 'is a factor of'.

Exercise 7.13

For each of the arrow graphs, find what the arrow means.

1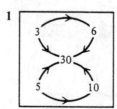

2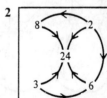

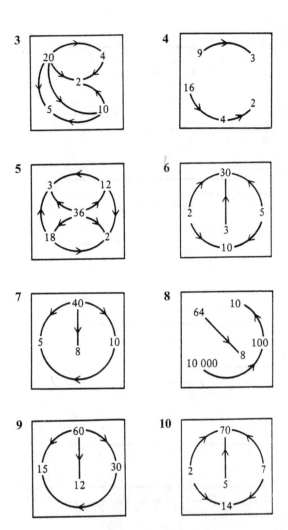

In the arrow graph below, ⟋ stands for 'is 1 less than'.

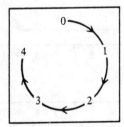

The same information is shown in this number line.

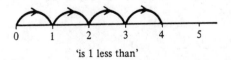

'is 1 less than'

A number line can also show the relation 'is greater than 2'.

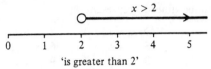

'is greater than 2'

This means that the number x can have any value that is greater than 2.

> means 'is greater than'
< means 'is less than'

Example 14

Draw a number line to show the relation 'is less than 5' or $x < 5$.

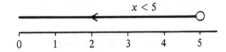

Exercise 7.14

Draw number lines to represent:
1 'is greater than 6' or $x > 6$
2 'is less than 6' or $x < 6$
3 'is greater than 8' or > 8
4 'is less than 8' or < 8
5 $x > 4$ 6 $x > 1$
7 $x > 12$ 8 $x < 3$
9 $x < 11$ 10 $x < 1$

⩾ means 'is greater than or equal to'
⩽ means 'is less than or equal to'

Example 15

Draw number lines to show the relation:
a $p \leqslant 5$
b $q > 3$

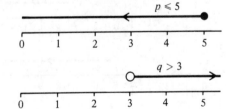

Note that:
in a ● means that 5 is included in the set of values.
in b ○ means that 3 is *not* included in the set of values.

56

Exercise 7.15

Draw number lines to represent:

1 $x > 10$	**2** $x > 13$	**3** $a > 11$
4 $b \geqslant 2$	**5** $x \geqslant 5$	**6** $m \geqslant 3$
7 $n \geqslant 6$	**8** $x < 8$	**9** $p < 7$
10 $q < 9$	**11** $x < 12$	**12** $x \leqslant 8$
13 $a \leqslant 2$	**14** $b \leqslant 10$	**15** $c \leqslant 7$
16 $2 < x$	**17** $3 > y$	**18** $y + 2 > 3$
19 $z - 2 < 4$	**20** $a - 4 \leqslant 3$	**21** $b + 1 \geqslant 4$

Example 16

Describe these number lines.

a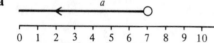

b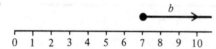

c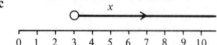

d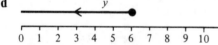

a $a < 7$	**b** $b \geqslant 7$
c $x > 3$	**d** $y \leqslant 6$

Exercise 7.16

Describe these number lines.

1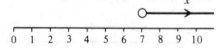

2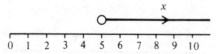

3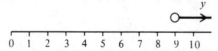

4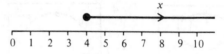

5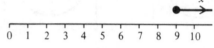

6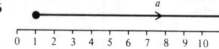

7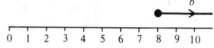

8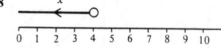

9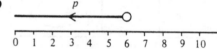

10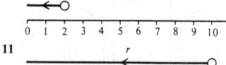

11

12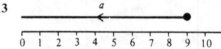

13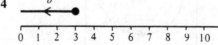

14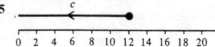

15

Unit 8 Bar charts and pictograms

Bar charts

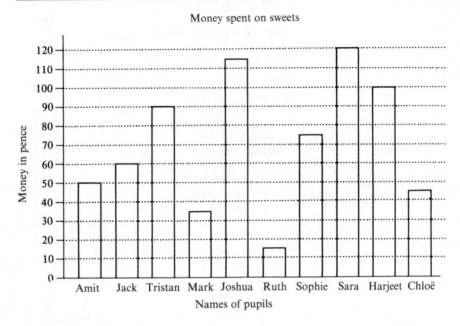

Money spent on sweets

The *bar chart* above shows the money spent on sweets in one week by 10 children.

To draw a bar chart:

1 Draw two lines at right angles to each other on the graph paper to form the axes, one vertical and one horizontal.
2 Divide these two axes into equal parts, using the scales given.
3 On the vertical axis label the points which mark the equal parts and give the axis a suitable title, e.g. Money in pence.
4 On the horizontal axis label the equal parts and give the axis a suitable title, e.g. Names of pupils.
5 Draw bars to illustrate the information given, leaving a space between each bar.
6 Give the chart a suitable title, e.g. Money spent on sweets

Example 1

The following table shows the money spent on sweets in one week by 10 children.

Name	Amit	Jack	Tristan	Mark	Joshua	Ruth	Sophie	Sara	Harjeet	Chloë
Amount in pence	50	60	90	35	115	15	75	120	100	45

Using a scale of 2 cm for each name on the horizontal axis and 1 cm to 10 p on the vertical axis, represent this information on a bar chart.

This chart is shown at the top of this page.

Exercise 8.1

1 The bar chart shows
how many people went
to a craft exhibition on
each day of a certain
week.

Find from the chart:

a the total number of
visitors for the
whole week.

b the money collected
on Saturday if the
admission charge is
£2.

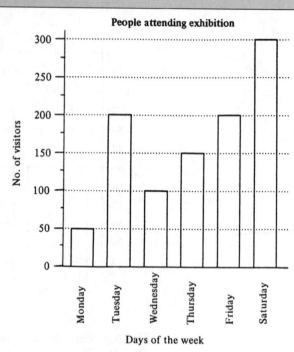

People attending exhibition

No. of visitors

Days of the week

2 The bar chart shows
how many pupils had a
school lunch on each
day of a certain week.

Find from the chart:

a the total number of
meals served during
the whole week.

b the total amount of
dinner money
collected for the
whole week if the
cost of a meal is
£1.05.

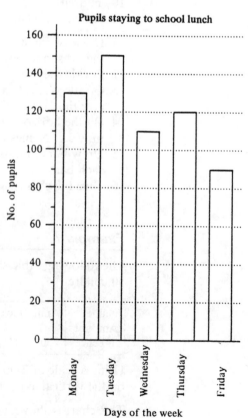

Pupils staying to school lunch

No. of pupils

Days of the week

3 The bar chart shows the numbers of different kinds of sandwiches that a snack bar sold on a certain day.

Find from the chart:

a the total number of sandwiches sold.
b the amount of money taken if all sandwiches sell at 80 p each.

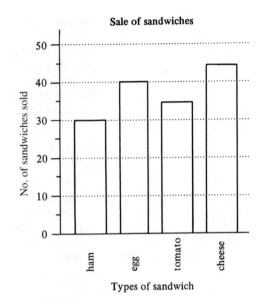

Sale of sandwiches

4 The bar chart shows how many cars used a ferry on each day of a certain week.

Find from the chart:

a the total number of cars that used the ferry during the whole week.
b the money taken on Saturday if the cost per car is £50.

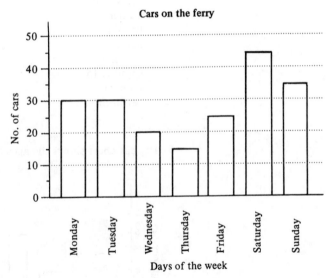

Cars on the ferry

5 The bar chart shows how many kilometres an athlete runs during her training on each day of a certain week.

Find from the chart:

a the total number of kilometres that she runs during the week.

b the total number of hours that she spends on her training if her average running speed is 15 kilometres per hour.

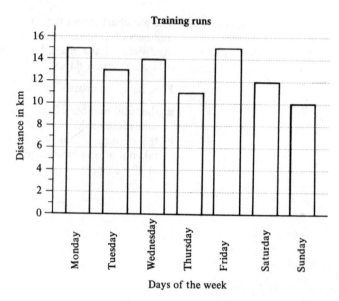

Training runs

6 The bar chart shows the ages of all the members of a ladies' hockey club.

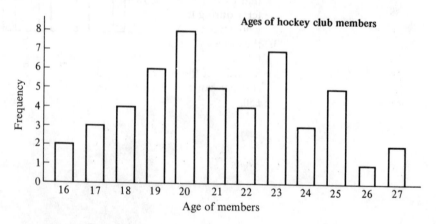

Ages of hockey club members

Find from the bar chart:

a the number of members who are
(i) 18, (ii) 20, (iii) 21, (iv) 23, (v) 24, (vi) 26 years of age.
b how many members are under 20 years of age.
c how many members are over 20 years of age.
d how many members the club has altogether.

7 The bar chart shows how many goals were scored by a football team in all their matches during the season.

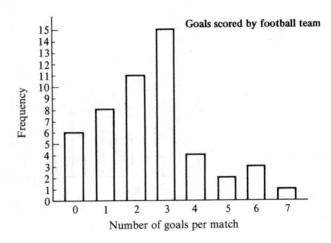

Find from the bar chart:

a in how many matches the team scored
   (i) no goals, (ii) 2 goals, (iii) 3 goals, (iv) 4 goals, (v) 6 goals.
b in how many matches the team scored less than 3 goals.
c in how many matches the team scored more than 3 goals.
d the number of matches the team played in the whole season.

8 The bar chart shows the size of shoe worn by each of the girls in class 3B.

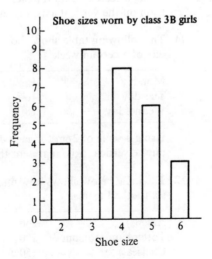

Find from the bar chart:

a how many girls wear shoes of sizes up to and including size 4.
b the number of girls in class 3B altogether.

9 The bar chart shows the scores that resulted from throwing two dice.

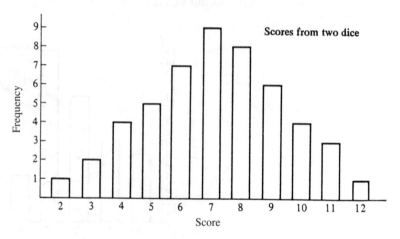

Find from the bar chart:

a how many times the score was 6 or greater.
b the number of times that the two dice were thrown altogether.

Suggest a reason why a score of 7 occurred more frequently than any other score.

10 The following table shows how many trains left London (Euston) for other cities on a certain afternoon.

Birmingham	7	Liverpool	4
Chester	1	Manchester	5
Glasgow	3		

Using a scale of 2 cm for each city name on the horizontal axis and 1 cm for one train on the vertical axis, represent this information on a bar chart.

11 The following table shows how many children were present in class 3B on each day of a certain week.

Monday	15	Thursday	20
Tuesday	16	Friday	19
Wednesday	18		

Using a scale of 2 cm for each day on the horizontal axis and 1 cm for one pupil on the vertical axis, represent this information on a bar chart.

12 The table below shows how many boys in a London school supported each of six football teams.

Arsenal	250	West Ham United	150
Tottenham Hotspur	200	Fulham	100
Chelsea	150	Queen's Park Rangers	50

Using a scale of 2 cm for the name of each football team on the horizontal axis and 1 cm to 10 boys on the vertical axis, represent this information on a bar chart.

13 The table below shows how many children in class 2A take each of five different sizes of shoe.

shoe size	1	2	3	4	5
number of children	4	9	10	5	2

Using a scale of 2 cm for each shoe-size number on the horizontal axis and 1 cm for one child on the vertical axis, display this information on a bar chart.

14 A boy throws a die twenty times. His scores are shown below.

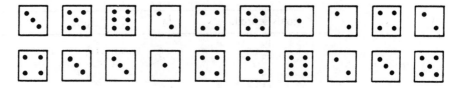

Using a scale of 2 cm for the number of each score on the horizontal axis and 1 cm for one throw on the vertical axis, display the scoring details on a bar chart.

15 At Orchard Road School there are ten classes. The table below shows how many pupils in each class are members of the school drama club.

class	1A	1B	2A	2B	3A	3B	4A	4B	5A	5B
no. of pupils	6	5	9	10	7	8	12	10	6	7

Using a scale of 1 cm for each form name on the horizontal axis and 1 cm for one pupil on the vertical axis, display this information on a bar chart.

Find from the details:
a the total number of pupils in the club.
b the amount of money paid into the club each term if the termly subscription from each pupil is £2.

16 In Oak Court there are ten flats. The table below shows how many bottles of milk the milkman delivers to each flat during a certain week.

Mrs Thompson	(No. 1)	14	Mr Morris	(No. 6)	7
Mr MacDonald	(No. 2)	7	Mrs Smith	(No. 7)	28
Mrs Green	(No. 3)	21	Mrs Cook	(No. 8)	21
Mrs Patel	(No. 4)	14	Mr Chavola	(No. 9)	10
Miss Carr	(No. 5)	14	Ms Scott	(No. 10)	14

Using a scale of 1 cm for each number of flat on the horizontal axis and 1 cm for one bottle of milk on the vertical axis, display this information on a bar chart.

Find from the details:
a the total number of bottles that the milkman delivers during the course of the week.
b the total amount of money that he collects at the end of the week if the price of one bottle is 37 p.

The following list gives the numbers of goals scored by thirty footballers during one season.

20	14	19	14	12	17	13	16	14	17
18	13	16	13	21	16	13	15	13	15
15	12	16	13	18	20	16	15	18	14

This information can be illustrated on a bar chart. The first step is to draw up a *tally chart* from the data to find the frequency of each number of goals scored.

goals scored	tally	frequency
12	//	2
13	̷H̷H̷ /	6
14	////	4
15	////	4
16	̷H̷H̷	5
17	//	2
18	///	3
19	/	1
20	//	2
21	/	1

total 30

Here is the bar chart for this data.

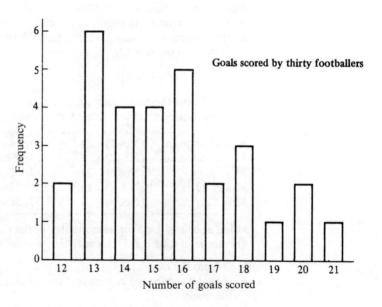

Goals scored by thirty footballers

Exercise 8.2

For each question draw up a tally chart; then display the information on a bar chart.

1 The list below gives the marks out of ten obtained by the pupils in Year 11 in a Science test.

3	6	5	7	1	8	6	7	8	4
7	8	3	0	9	7	2	3	5	6
5	9	7	8	10	4	1	6	7	6

2 The marks obtained by each pupil in class 5A in a French test are shown below.

2	6	4	6	5	7	2	3	8	5
5	2	7	1	3	8	5	9	4	7
3	7	1	8	9	0	7	6	2	8

3 The list shows the number of bottles of milk delivered to each house in Park Close.

3	1	3	2	4	2	1
2	4	3	5	2	1	6
4	5	2	3	1	2	

4 The list gives the outside temperature in degrees Celsius on each of the thirty days in April.

5	4	5	8	10	7	6	9	6	2
2	1	0	0	3	4	5	4	6	8
10	10	8	7	5	6	9	7	4	5

5 The number of cars sold by a garage salesman on each of the thirty days in June is shown below.

2	4	1	0	3	1	2	0	1	4
5	3	1	2	0	3	4	1	0	2
0	1	4	3	1	2	0	3	5	2

6 The list below shows the number of pupils in each of the twenty-five classes at Ash Green School.

26	28	27	28	25	29	28	25	29
27	28	25	29	27	26	29	28	26
29	25	29	28	28	27	25		

Statistical facts are often displayed by means of an illustration. This is especially so in advertisements.

A *pictogram* is one type of illustration; it uses an appropriate symbol to represent a specific number of items.

Pictograms

Example 2

The number of cups of drink that were dispensed from a vending machine during the course of a certain day was as follows.

type of drink	tea	coffee	cocoa	soup	milk	squash
no. dispensed	108	84	36	60	24	48

Illustrate this information on a suitable pictogram.

An appropriate symbol for this would be ⊔ to represent 12 drinks dispensed.
The pictogram is shown below.

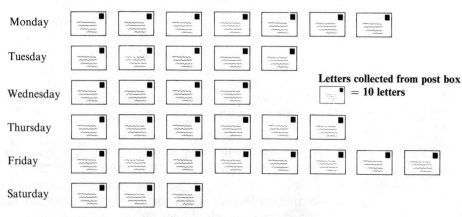

Drinks dispensed from vending machine
⊔ = 12 drinks

Exercise 8.3

1 The pictogram below shows how many letters were collected from a post box on each of the days of a certain week.

Monday

Tuesday

Wednesday

Thursday

Friday

Saturday

Letters collected from post box
▣ = 10 letters

If the symbol ▣ represents 10 letters, find the total number of letters collected from the post box over the whole week.

2 The pictogram below shows how many baskets of apples a picker fills during each week of a four-week period.

If the symbol ⬮ represents 4 filled baskets, find:

a the total number of basketfuls that he picks.
b the total amount that he earns if he is paid £15 for every basket that he fills.

3 The pictogram below shows how many people travelled from Newcastle to Alnwick by bus on each of the days of a certain week.

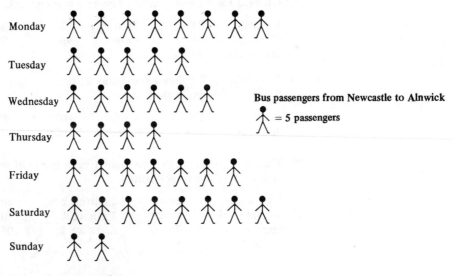

If the symbol 大 represents 5 passengers, find:

a the total number of passengers who made the journey during the course of the week.
b the total amount of money that the passengers paid to the bus operator if the fare is £3.00 per passenger.

In questions **4** to **10**, display the given information on a pictogram. First choose a simple symbol to represent a certain number of items.

4 The list below shows how many pairs of shoes a shoe shop sold on each of the days of a certain week.

Monday	30	Thursday	30
Tuesday	50	Friday	40
Wednesday	20	Saturday	60

5 The list below shows how many pupils there are in each of the five classes at a village junior school.

Class 1	25	Class 3	20	Class 5	25
Class 2	30	Class 4	15		

6 The details below show how many cars were parked at a station car park on each of the days of a certain week.

Monday	20	Thursday	12	Saturday	32
Tuesday	24	Friday	28	Sunday	8
Wednesday	16				

7 The list below shows how many keys were cut at a 'While you wait' counter on each of the days of a certain week.

Monday	24	Wednesday	18	Friday	30
Tuesday	42	Thursday	36	Saturday	48

8 The list below shows how many bottles of milk were delivered to the houses in Orchard Lane on each of the days of a certain week.

Monday	84	Thursday	72	Saturday	108
Tuesday	96	Friday	96	Sunday	60
Wednesday	72				

9 The following list shows how many ice creams were sold on each of the days of the Easter holiday period.

Friday	120	Sunday	160	Tuesday	80
Saturday	100	Monday	180		

10 The details below show how many trees a group of woodcutters felled during each week of a six-week period.

First week	60	Fourth week	60
Second week	45	Fifth week	90
Third week	75	Sixth week	105

Grouping data

One hundred pupils took a Mathematics test marked out of 20. These are their scores.

1	1	1	2	2	2	2	3	3	3
3	3	4	4	4	4	5	5	5	5
5	5	6	6	6	6	7	7	7	7
7	7	7	8	8	8	8	9	9	9
9	9	10	10	11	11	11	11	12	12
12	12	12	13	13	13	13	13	13	14
14	14	14	14	14	14	14	14	15	15
15	15	15	15	15	15	15	16	16	16
16	16	16	16	17	17	17	17	17	18
18	18	18	19	19	19	19	20	20	20

This data could be illustrated with a bar chart like this:

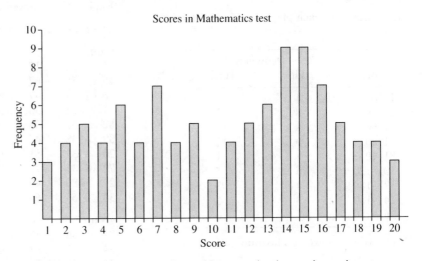

This bar chart has a large number of bars and takes quite a time to construct. It may be preferable to *group* the data into a table like this:

score	1–4	5–8	9–12	13–16	17–20
frequency	16	21	16	31	16

This is a bar chart for the grouped scores.

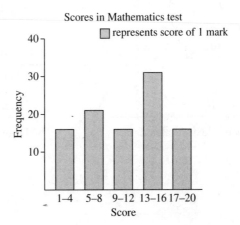

Exercise 8.4

1 Make a table for the 100 marks using groups 1–2, 3–4, 5–6, 7–8, 9–10 and so on.
   Draw a bar chart to illustrate your table.

2 Make a table for the 100 marks using groups 1–5, 6–10 and so on.
   Draw a bar chart to illustrate your table.

3 Two darts players, Bill and Terri, both throw three darts 50 times.

The 50 scores for each player are shown in this table.

	frequency	
score	Bill	Terri
1–20	4	1
21–40	8	12
41–60	8	14
61–80	9	12
81–100	8	1
101–120	5	5
121–140	4	3
141–160	3	2
161–180	1	0

Draw two bar charts to illustrate this data.

4 The weekly incomes of two groups of fifty people are shown in this table

	frequency	
income (£)	group 1	group 2
0–50	2	0
51–100	3	0
101–150	7	2
151–200	10	8
201–250	18	13
251–300	7	17
301–350	2	7
351–400	1	3

Draw two bar charts to illustrate this data.

5 Two groups of 80 students are compared on an English test, marked out of 100.

The results are shown in these lists:

group 1
15	12	17	64	56	67	51	89
45	56	67	34	92	28	31	32
36	74	47	83	87	98	89	21
11	23	33	34	56	35	47	68
82	42	34	45	31	47	33	56
39	38	47	36	46	37	65	70
20	32	51	62	52	53	54	67
72	81	77	83	85	37	36	36
29	80	40	53	33	33	34	51
30	63	66	55	44	33	71	70

group 2
21	56	57	62	73	82	83	90
34	57	83	66	74	74	57	60
34	56	71	79	73	74	56	63
64	81	88	92	99	34	35	63
22	82	20	90	65	56	72	77
75	23	34	43	56	65	67	76
80	81	45	59	92	85	75	73
62	64	68	66	74	73	77	78
23	39	47	74	77	82	94	90
38	49	60	55	55	73	77	82

a Collect this data into a table with these headings:

	frequency	
mark	group 1	group 2
1–10		
11–20		
etc.		

b Draw two bar charts to illustrate this data.

Unit 9 Multiplying and dividing II

These are important number facts which are practised in this unit.

	1	2	3	4	5	6	7	8	9	10
1	1	2	3	4	5	6	7	8	9	10
2	2	4	6	8	10	12	14	16	18	20
3	3	6	9	12	15	18	21	24	27	30
4	4	8	12	16	20	24	28	32	36	40
5	5	10	15	20	25	30	35	40	45	50
6	6	12	18	24	30	36	42	48	54	60
7	7	14	21	28	35	42	49	56	63	70
8	8	16	24	32	40	48	56	64	72	80
9	9	18	27	36	45	54	63	72	81	90
10	10	20	30	40	50	60	70	80	90	100

Multiplying

Example 1

Multiply and find the 'odd answer out'.

a 6×6 **b** 5×7 **c** 12×3 **d** 4×9

a 6×6	**b** 5×7	**c** 12×3	**d** 4×9
$= 36$	$= 35$	$= 36$	$= 36$

So **b** is the 'odd answer out' because its answer is 35.

Exercise 9.1

Multiply the following to find the 'odd answer out'.

1 a 8×3 **b** 5×5 **c** 6×4 **d** 2×12

2 a 5×4 **3 a** 7×2 **4 a** 4×5
  b 3×7 **b** 3×4 **b** 9×2
  c 10×2 **c** 2×6 **c** 3×6

5 a 6×8 **6 a** 4×10 **7 a** 3×5
  b 12×4 **b** 7×6 **b** 2×8
  c 7×7 **c** 8×5 **c** 4×4

8 a 10×7 **9 a** 3×10 **10 a** 12×5
  b 8×9 **b** 6×5 **b** 7×9
  c 6×12 **c** 8×4 **c** 6×10

Example 2

Multiply to find the 'odd answer out'.

a 49×6 **b** 42×7 **c** 38×8

a 49	**b** 42	**c** 38
$\times 6$	$\times 7$	$\times 8$
294	294	304

So **c** is the 'odd answer out' because its answer is 304.

Exercise 9.2

Multiply the following to find the 'odd answer out'.

1 a 24×4 **2 a** 15×6 **3 a** 57×4
  b 16×6 **b** 23×4 **b** 76×3
  c 14×7 **c** 18×5 **c** 34×7

4 a 34×8 **5 a** 15×7 **6 a** 98×4
  b 36×7 **b** 27×5 **b** 56×7
  c 84×3 **c** 45×3 **c** 38×9

7 a 35×9 **8 a** 14×8 **9 a** 22×7
  b 67×5 **b** 17×6 **b** 16×9
  c 45×7 **c** 16×7 **c** 18×8

10 a 285×3 **11 a** 197×4 **12 a** 78×9
  b 125×7 **b** 266×3 **b** 178×4
  c 175×5 **c** 114×7 **c** 117×6

13 a 119×8 **14 a** 153×5 **15 a** 124×7
  b 314×3 **b** 85×9 **b** 207×4
  c 136×7 **c** 105×7 **c** 138×6

To multiply by 20, first multiply by 10 and then by 2.

To multiply by 500, first multiply by 100 and then by 5.

Example 3

Multiply the following:

a 32×30 **b** 27×600

a $32 \times 30 = 320 \times 3$ **b** $27 \times 600 = 2700 \times 6$
           $= 960$ $= 16\,200$

Exercise 9.3

1 36×20	**2** 13×50	**3** 14×60
4 16×70	**5** 24×80	**6** 135×30
7 216×40	**8** 121×70	**9** 142×60
10 156×50	**11** 90×30	**12** 80×60
13 400×20	**14** 700×50	**15** 28×200
16 32×300	**17** 38×600	**18** 148×200
19 232×400	**20** 136×500	**21** 104×700
22 105×800	**23** 240×300	**24** 160×600

Example 4

Find the product of:

a 43 and 27   **b** 104 and 16

You can use a calculator, or find the answers like this:

a

43	
$\times 27$	
860	(43×20)
301	(43×7)
1161	

b

104	
$\times 16$	
624	(104×6)
1040	(104×10)
1664	

Exercise 9.4

1 45×13	**2** 24×16	**3** 32×18
4 38×17	**5** 57×15	**6** 29×14
7 32×24	**8** 42×26	**9** 132×14
10 125×13		

Multiply the following to find the 'odd answer out'.

11 a 21×16 **12 a** 34×18
   b 19×18 **b** 32×19
   c 24×14 **c** 51×12

13 a 62×11 **14 a** 36×15
   b 48×14 **b** 35×16
   c 42×16 **c** 40×14

15 a 28×24 **16 a** 32×27
   b 32×21 **b** 31×28
   c 31×22 **c** 36×24

17 a 46×33 **18 a** 42×24
   b 42×36 **b** 39×26
   c 54×28 **c** 36×28

19 a 135×14 **20 a** 114×17
   b 124×15 **b** 102×19
   c 105×18 **c** 137×14

If you are asked the question:

What is 79×53?

You can find an answer in three ways:

a with a calculator:

$\boxed{7}\;\boxed{9}\;\boxed{\times}\;\boxed{5}\;\boxed{3}\;\boxed{=}$ 4187

b with pen and paper:

79	
53	
3950	(79×50)
237	(79×3)
4187	(79×53)

c with an estimated approximate answers:

79×53 is approximately 80×50

80×50 is $8 \times 5 \times 10 \times 10 = 4000$

79×53 is approximately 4000

To estimate approximate answers:

leave numbers between 1 and 10 unchanged,
round numbers between 10 and 99 to the nearest 10,
round numbers between 100 and 999 to the nearest 100.

Example 5

Estimate approximate answers for:

a 7×19 **b** 23×38 **c** 467×72

a 7×19 is approximately $7 \times 20 = 140$

b 23×38 is approximately $20 \times 40 = 800$

c 467×72 is approximately $500 \times 70 = 35\,000$

Exercise 9.5

Estimate approximate answers for the following. Find an accurate answer using either pen and paper or a calculator.

1 18×6	**2** 34×9	**3** 2×92
4 8×76	**5** 12×52	**6** 7×59
7 57×9	**8** 14×25	**9** 54×43
10 96×69	**11** 37×82	**12** 296×24

13 372×51 **14** 649×77 **15** 45×712
16 $35 \times 41 \times 29$ **17** $27 \times 82 \times 51$
18 $19 \times 7 \times 33$ **19** $23 \times 121 \times 56$
20 259×307 **21** 776×911
22 356×298 **23** 230×411
24 573×781 **25** $6 \times 85 \times 178 \times 203$

When you find answers using a calculator, you can check them using *inverse operations*.

Example 6

Multiply with a calculator and check the answer with an inverse operation.

a 79×8 **b** 127×65

a $79 \times 8 = 632$
     Check: $632 \div 8 = 79$

b $127 \times 65 = 8255$
     Check: $8255 \div 65 = 127$

Example 7

Find an appropriate answer and an accurate answer for 897×45.
Check your accurate answer with an inverse operation.

897×45 is approximately $900 \times 50 = 45\,000$

$897 \times 45 = 40\,365$

Check: $40\,365 \div 45 = 897$

Exercise 9.6

Find an appropriate answer and an accurate answer for the following.
Check your accurate answer with an inverse operation.

 1 5×63 **2** 85×4 **3** 65×6
 4 8×79 **5** 27×72 **6** 83×38
 7 44×27 **8** 39×17 **9** 45×31
10 405×72 **11** 831×16
12 550×13 **13** 92×896
14 65×624 **15** 83×167
16 234×423 **17** 171×717
18 362×263 **19** 623×632
20 326×236 **21** 459×495
22 549×594 **23** 945×954
24 999×111 **25** 450×549

Example 8

A market gardener plants 27 rows of potatoes and puts 42 potatoes in each row.
How many potatoes does she plant altogether?

Number of potatoes planted $= 27 \times 42$

$$
\begin{array}{r}
27 \\
\times 42 \\
\hline
1080 \quad (27 \times 40) \\
54 \quad (27 \times 2) \\
\hline
1134
\end{array}
$$

The market gardener planted 1134 potatoes.

Exercise 9.7

1 How high is the wall if each brick is 8 cm in height?

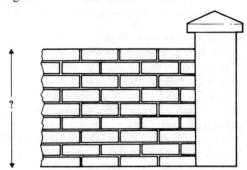

2 The distance from Dover to Calais is 32 kilometres.
What is:
  a the distance from Newhaven to Dieppe if it is 3 times as far,
  b the distance from Weymouth to St. Helier if it is 4 times as far?

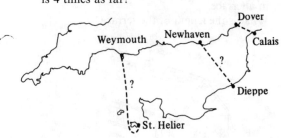

3 Walton Hill, near Halesowen, is 316 metres above sea level. Helvellyn in Cumbria is three times this height.
What is the height of Helvellyn?

4 What is the length of this viaduct?

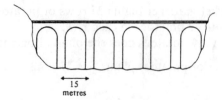

15
metres

5 How many small panes are there in the windows at the front of this school building?

LEA ROAD SCHOOL

6 A railway locomotive is pulling a train of 12 coaches each of which has 8 wheels.
If the locomotive also has 8 wheels, how many wheels are rolling altogether?

7 A van delivers 5 cases of lemonade cans to a shop. If each case contains 24 cans, how many are delivered?

8 In a new office building 35 doors are required. If each door is fastened by means of 3 hinges, how many hinges are needed?
What is the total number of screws that are required if each hinge has 6 screw-holes?

9 During a certain week 26 lorry loads of stone were removed from a quarry.
If each lorry carried 15 tonnes, how many tonnes of stone were removed?

10 The house illustrated is the first of 25 similar ones in a terrace.
What is the length of the terrace?

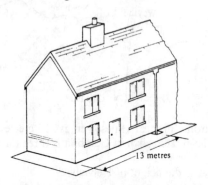

13 metres

Dividing

Example 9

Using division find the 'odd answer out'.

a $72 \div 8$ **b** $81 \div 9$ **c** $36 \div 4$ **d** $56 \div 7$

a $\dfrac{9}{8)72}$ b $\dfrac{9}{9)81}$ c $\dfrac{9}{4)36}$ d $\dfrac{8}{7)56}$

So **d** is the 'odd answer out' because its answer is 8.

Exercise 9.8

Divide the following to find the 'odd answer out'.

1	**a** $42 \div 7$	**2**	**a** $54 \div 6$	**3**	**a** $18 \div 3$
	b $56 \div 8$		**b** $24 \div 3$		**b** $54 \div 9$
	c $30 \div 5$		**c** $32 \div 4$		**c** $36 \div 6$
	d $24 \div 4$		**d** $72 \div 9$		**d** $35 \div 7$
4	**a** $63 \div 9$	**5**	**a** $45 \div 9$	**6**	**a** $42 \div 3$
	b $48 \div 6$		**b** $15 \div 3$		**b** $98 \div 7$
	c $64 \div 8$		**c** $48 \div 8$		**c** $84 \div 6$
	d $40 \div 5$		**d** $25 \div 5$		**d** $52 \div 4$
7	**a** $78 \div 6$	**8**	**a** $96 \div 6$	**9**	**a** $85 \div 5$
	b $56 \div 4$		**b** $68 \div 4$		**b** $51 \div 3$
	c $65 \div 5$		**c** $48 \div 3$		**c** $72 \div 4$
	d $91 \div 7$		**d** $80 \div 5$		**d** $34 \div 2$
10	**a** $76 \div 4$	**11**	**a** $36 \div 3$	**12**	**a** $38 \div 2$
	b $36 \div 2$		**b** $84 \div 7$		**b** $95 \div 5$
	c $54 \div 3$		**c** $96 \div 8$		**c** $64 \div 4$
	d $90 \div 5$		**d** $70 \div 5$		**d** $57 \div 3$

Example 10

Using division find the 'odd answer out'.

a $224 \div 7$ **b** $256 \div 8$ **c** $165 \div 5$

a $\begin{array}{r} 32 \\ 7)\overline{224} \\ 21 \\ \hline 14 \\ 14 \\ \hline \end{array}$ (7×3) (7×2)

b $\begin{array}{r} 32 \\ 8)\overline{256} \\ 24 \\ \hline 16 \\ 16 \\ \hline \end{array}$ (3×8) (2×8)

c $\begin{array}{r} 33 \\ 5)\overline{165} \\ 15 \\ \hline 15 \\ 15 \\ \hline \end{array}$ (5×3) (5×3)

So **c** has the 'odd answer out' because its answer is 33.

Exercise 9.9

Divide the following to find the 'odd answer out'.

1	a	$195 \div 5$	2	a	$144 \div 4$	3	a	$288 \div 6$
	b	$117 \div 3$		b	$252 \div 7$		b	$376 \div 8$
	c	$259 \div 7$		c	$216 \div 6$		c	$336 \div 7$
	d	$312 \div 8$		d	$306 \div 9$		d	$240 \div 5$
4	a	$210 \div 5$	5	a	$366 \div 6$	6	a	$488 \div 4$
	b	$126 \div 3$		b	$248 \div 4$		b	$336 \div 3$
	c	$168 \div 4$		c	$549 \div 9$		c	$784 \div 7$
	d	$287 \div 7$		d	$305 \div 5$			
7	a	$369 \div 3$	8	a	$585 \div 5$	9	a	$847 \div 7$
	b	$791 \div 7$		b	$381 \div 3$		b	$524 \div 4$
	c	$565 \div 5$		c	$468 \div 4$		c	$655 \div 5$
10	a	$476 \div 2$	11	a	$952 \div 8$	12	a	$660 \div 5$
	b	$714 \div 3$		b	$645 \div 5$		b	$852 \div 6$
	c	$992 \div 4$		c	$714 \div 6$		c	$924 \div 7$
13	a	$696 \div 6$	14	a	$545 \div 5$	15	a	$640 \div 4$
	b	$742 \div 7$		b	$981 \div 9$		b	$540 \div 3$
	c	$954 \div 9$		c	$476 \div 4$		c	$800 \div 5$

Example 11

Work out the following divisions:

a $576 \div 18$ **b** $920 \div 23$ **c** $653 \div 31$

You can use a calculator or find the answers like this:

```
a      32                    b      40
   18)576                       23)920
       54   (18 × 3)               92   (23 × 4)
       36                          00
       36   (18 × 2)               00   (23 × 0)

c      21
   31)653
       62   (31 × 2)
       33
       31   (31 × 1)
        2   remainder
```

Therefore, $576 \div 18 = 32$
                $920 \div 23 = 40$
                $653 \div 31 = 21$ r2

Exercise 9.10

1 $195 \div 13$	2 $182 \div 14$	3 $276 \div 23$
4 $384 \div 16$	5 $483 \div 21$	6 $768 \div 24$
7 $992 \div 32$	8 $780 \div 26$	9 $810 \div 18$
10 $672 \div 16$	11 $756 \div 14$	12 $945 \div 15$

Divide the following to find the 'odd answer out'.

13	a	$182 \div 13$	14	a	$224 \div 16$	15	a	$176 \div 11$
	b	$221 \div 17$		b	$266 \div 19$		b	$204 \div 12$
	c	$234 \div 18$		c	$210 \div 14$		c	$208 \div 13$
16	a	$225 \div 17$	17	a	$299 \div 13$	18	a	$378 \div 18$
	b	$240 \div 15$		b	$345 \div 15$		b	$374 \div 17$
	c	$270 \div 18$		c	$384 \div 16$		c	$418 \div 19$
19	a	$294 \div 21$	20	a	$504 \div 21$	21	a	$792 \div 24$
	b	$336 \div 24$		b	$506 \div 22$		b	$672 \div 21$
	c	$276 \div 23$		c	$600 \div 25$		c	$832 \div 26$
22	a	$748 \div 22$	23	a	$900 \div 25$	24	a	$720 \div 15$
	b	$864 \div 27$		b	$910 \div 26$		b	$864 \div 18$
	c	$782 \div 23$		c	$980 \div 28$		c	$784 \div 16$

Find the answer and remainder for each of the following.

25 $159 \div 12$	26 $310 \div 20$	27 $360 \div 25$
28 $204 \div 15$	29 $184 \div 16$	30 $222 \div 18$

If you are asked the question:

What is $985 \div 47$?

You can find an answer in three ways:

a with a calculator:

$$\boxed{9}\,\boxed{8}\,\boxed{5}\,\boxed{\div}\,\boxed{4}\,\boxed{7}\,\boxed{=}\ \text{20.957449}$$

$47 \times 20 = 940$

$985 - 940 = 45$

$985 \div 47 = 20$ remainder 45

b with an estimated approximate answer:

$985 \div 47$ is approximately $1000 \div 50$

$1000 \div 50 = 100 \div 5 = 20$

$985 \div 47$ is approximately 20

c with pen and paper:

```
      20
  47)985
     94
     45
     00
     45   remainder
```

$985 \div 47 = 20$ remainder 45.

Example 12

Estimate approximate answers for the following:

a $74 \div 34$ **b** $684 \div 57$ **c** $627 \div 23$

a $74 \div 34$ is approximately $70 \div 30$
     $= 7 \div 3$ which is approximately 2

b $684 \div 57$ is approximately $700 \div 60$
     $= 70 \div 6$ which is approximately 12

c $627 \div 23$ is approximately $600 \div 20$
     $= 60 \div 2 = 30$

Exercise 9.11

Estimate approximate answers for the following questions. Then find an accurate answer using either pen and paper or a calculator.

1	$96 \div 16$	2	$95 \div 19$
3	$192 \div 24$	4	$715 \div 13$
5	$275 \div 25$	6	$504 \div 56$
7	$858 \div 22$	8	$858 \div 39$
9	$817 \div 19$	10	$279 \div 31$
11	$335 \div 67$	12	$538 \div 24$
13	$438 \div 38$	14	$632 \div 33$
15	$868 \div 37$	16	$377 \div 29$
17	$390 \div 42$	18	$890 \div 19$
19	$661 \div 42$	20	$427 \div 26$

When you find answers with a calculator, you can check them using *inverse operations*.

Example 13

Divide with a calculator and check the answer with an inverse operation.

a $79 \div 8$ **b** $127 \div 65$

a $79 \div 8 = 9.875$

    Check: $9.875 \times 8 = 79$

b $127 \div 65 = 1.953\,846\,2$

    Check: $1.953\,846\,2 \times 65 = 127$

Example 14

Find an approximate answer and an accurate answer for $897 \div 45$.
Check your accurate answer with an inverse operation.

$897 \div 45$ is approximately $900 \div 50$

    $= 90 \div 5 = 18$

$897 \div 45 = 19.933\,333$

Check: $19.93\,333 \times 45 = 897$

$45 \times 19 = 855$

$897 - 855 = 42$

$897 \div 45 = 19$ remainder 42

Exercise 9.12

Find an approximate answer and an accurate answer for the following.
Check your accurate answer with an inverse operation.

1	$923 \div 34$	2	$798 \div 37$
3	$302 \div 21$	4	$259 \div 13$
5	$721 \div 22$	6	$587 \div 33$
7	$602 \div 39$	8	$941 \div 19$
9	$826 \div 13$	10	$99 \div 21$
11	$998 \div 46$	12	$957 \div 36$
13	$985 \div 101$	14	$587 \div 195$
15	$783 \div 351$	16	$938 \div 384$
17	$597 \div 14$	18	$651 \div 15$
19	$921 \div 35$	20	$276 \div 56$

Example 15

How many jars of instant coffee each containing 58 grams can be filled from a carton containing 1000 grams?
How much coffee is left?

Number of jars $= 1000 \div 58$

$$
\begin{array}{r}
17 \\
58\overline{)1000} \\
\underline{58} \quad (58 \times 1) \\
420 \\
\underline{406} \quad (58 \times 7) \\
\underline{14} \quad \text{remainder}
\end{array}
$$

Therefore 17 jars can be filled and 14 grams are left.

Exercise 9.13

1 The bottle contains 620 millilitres of lemonade and its contents exactly fill all of the glasses shown.
What is the capacity of each of the glasses?

2 A poultry farmer has 396 eggs which are to be placed in cartons containing 6 eggs each.
How many cartons will he need?

3 Jack's birthday is 133 days after Aisha's.
How many weeks are there between their birthdays?

4 A multi-storey block has 104 flats altogether and there are 8 flats on each floor.
How many storeys does the building have?

5 A pipe-line is to be laid from a village to a nearby reservoir 960 metres away.
If the pipes are each of length 15 metres, how many will be needed?

6 In this gate the spaces between the wooden planks are the same width as the planks.
What is the width of each of the planks?

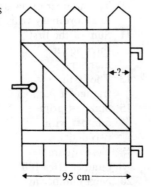

95 cm

7 The distance by rail from London to Carmarthen is 357 kilometres.
If the stations shown are equally spaced, what is the distance from Swindon to Cardiff?

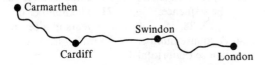

Carmarthen
Swindon
Cardiff
London

8 A van weighs 2000 kg when unloaded and 2360 kg when loaded with 8 bags of coal.
What is the weight of each bag?

9 An egg carton, which can hold 12 eggs, weighs 20 g when empty and 440 g when full.
What is the weight of each egg?

10 A warehouse manager orders 2400 tins of baked beans. They arrive on a lorry which is carrying 50 boxes of tins.
How many tins are there in each box?

11 The track through West Hill Tunnel is laid with steel rails of length 20 metres.
How many rails are there between one end of the tunnel and the other?

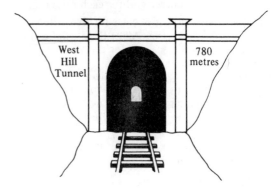

12 I drive my car from London to Birmingham and use 14 litres of petrol in doing so.
If the distance is 196 kilometres, how far can my car travel on one litre of petrol?

13 A library shelf is 120 cm long and 24 books of equal thickness fit exactly on it.
What is the thickness of each book?

14 Mrs Williams has made 1000 ml of jam and she wishes to put it into small jars which each have a capacity of 60 ml.
How many full jars will there be?
How many millilitres will there be in the one jar which will not be full?

15 A train is to move 300 tonnes of coal from a colliery to a power station.
If the wagons can carry 18 tonnes each, how many full wagons will there be?
How many tonnes will there be in the one wagon which will not be full?

The four number rules

Exercise 9.14

Copy the cross-number grid for each question.

The questions below give clues for five different 'cross-number' exercises. All of them can be answered on the above grid.

a *Across*
1 $32 + 41 + 13$
3 $16 + 22 + 24$
6 $13 + 16 + 23$
8 $121 + 113 + 141$
11 $18 + 23 + 5$
13 $28 + 16 + 9$
15 $19 + 48 + 27$
18 $183 + 131 + 111$
20 $105 + 112 + 119$
22 $46 + 29 + 7$
23 $145 + 228 + 264$
24 $323 + 98 + 135$

Down
2 $79 - 14$
4 $98 - 75$
5 $53 - 28$
7 $92 - 68$
9 $84 - 9$
10 $567 - 313$
12 $88 - 19$
14 $80 - 48$
16 $229 - 186$
17 $173 - 127$
19 $725 - 138$
21 $837 - 492$

b *Across*
1 $59 - 25$
3 $97 - 44$
6 $94 - 18$
8 $898 - 246$
11 $87 - 19$
13 $237 - 192$
15 $165 - 126$
18 $481 - 228$
20 $608 - 261$
22 $95 - 8$
23 $613 - 184$
24 $820 - 236$

Down
2 $14 + 21 + 12$
4 $17 + 15 + 4$
5 $13 + 42 + 37$
7 $27 + 30 + 9$
9 $5 + 23 + 27$
10 $212 + 123 + 107$
12 $62 + 13 + 8$
14 $9 + 8 + 38$
16 $29 + 47 + 17$
17 $56 + 9 + 22$
19 $152 + 161 + 76$
21 $223 + 79 + 156$

c *Across*
1 9×8
3 12×7
6 15×5
8 142×6

11 14×7
13 46×2
15 29×3
18 98×9

20 155×4
22 18×5
23 72×13
24 32×24

Down
2 $81 \div 3$
4 $384 \div 8$
5 $224 \div 7$

d *Across*
1 $95 \div 5$
3 $228 \div 6$
6 $679 \div 7$
8 $950 \div 2$
11 $276 \div 4$
13 $979 \div 11$
15 $826 \div 14$
18 $807 \div 3$
20 $768 \div 4$
22 $810 \div 18$
23 $960 \div 5$
24 $984 \div 8$

7 $295 \div 5$
9 $504 \div 9$
10 $792 \div 4$
12 $528 \div 6$
14 $336 \div 12$
16 $988 \div 13$
17 $900 \div 15$
19 $888 \div 3$
21 $944 \div 4$

Down
2 11×9
4 14×6
5 17×5
7 19×4
9 26×3
10 126×7
12 19×5
14 16×6
16 13×7
17 23×4
19 157×6
21 54×18

e *Across*
1 Smallest square number with two digits.
3 The fifth triangular number.
6 The square number which is just less than 50.
8 The number of days in an ordinary year.
11 Sum of the first three square numbers.
13 The sixth triangular number.
15 Smallest prime number with two digits.
18 Next square number after 100.
20 Next number in the sequence: 77, 88, 99, . . .
22 The fourth triangular number.
23 Next number in the sequence: 7, 14, 28, 56, . . .
24 A square number whose digits total 1.

Down
2 Next square number after the answer to 6 across.
4 The first prime number which is bigger than 50.
5 It is a square number, but it is not rectangular as well.
7 Sum of the first six square numbers.
9 The first prime number which is bigger than 60.
10 Same as 18 across.
12 The first prime number which is bigger than 40.
14 It is commonly called 'a dozen'.
16 The fifth prime number.
17 Next number in the sequence: 15, 30, 45, . . .
19 Same as 23 across.
21 The number of years in a century.

Example 16

Find the numbers to replace the * in each of the following.

a   4*6
      23*
 + *42
   1099

b   6**8
 − *49*
   4107

Here are the completed answers.

a   426
    231
 + 442
   1099

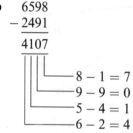

$$6 + 1 + 2 = 9$$
$$2 + 3 + 4 = 9$$
$$4 + 2 + 4 = 10$$

b   6598
 − 2491
   4107

$$8 - 1 = 7$$
$$9 - 9 = 0$$
$$5 - 4 = 1$$
$$6 - 2 = 4$$

Exercise 9.15

1 $313 + 442 + 124$
2 $353 + 121 + 252$
3 $245 + 336 + 403$
4 $465 + 246 + 154$
5 $547 + 323 + 56$
6 $633 + 40 + 78$

Find the 'odd answer out' for questions **7** to **18**.

7 **a** $232 + 413 + 123$
    b $241 + 385 + 132$
    c $226 + 404 + 128$
    d $335 + 118 + 305$

8 **a** $259 + 171 + 416$
    b $338 + 374 + 134$
    c $187 + 536 + 123$
    d $315 + 409 + 112$

9 **a** $375 + 405 + 163$
    b $697 + 142 + 104$
    c $516 + 185 + 252$
    d $352 + 260 + 331$

10 **a** $385 + 173 + 254$
     b $549 + 116 + 137$
     c $257 + 317 + 228$
     d $188 + 478 + 136$

11 **a** $343 + 231 + 23$
     b $264 + 240 + 83$
     c $438 + 112 + 47$
     d $227 + 305 + 65$

12 **a** $385 + 203 + 64$
     b $107 + 452 + 93$
     c $275 + 300 + 87$
     d $570 + 38 + 44$

13 **a** $130 + 53 + 16$
     b $155 + 32 + 12$
     c $48 + 87 + 54$
     d $96 + 98 + 5$

14 **a** $127 + 12 + 26$
     b $114 + 43 + 8$
     c $76 + 54 + 35$
     d $63 + 72 + 40$

15 **a** $36 + 95 + 16$
     b $99 + 53 + 5$
     c $118 + 32 + 7$
     d $101 + 52 + 4$

16 **a** $3476 + 1213$
     b $2945 + 1734$
     c $2392 + 2297$
     d $3836 + 853$

17 **a** $2388 + 1257$
     b $1969 + 1676$
     c $2855 + 790$
     d $2841 + 904$

18 **a** $2996 + 1854$
     b $3383 + 1467$
     c $1738 + 2842$
     d $3941 + 909$

19 $657 - 234$
20 $526 - 281$
21 $447 - 293$
22 $518 - 467$
23 $883 - 559$
24 $434 - 158$

Find the 'odd answer out' for questions **25** to **32**.

25 **a** $988 - 426$
     b $845 - 293$
     c $729 - 167$
     d $933 - 371$

26 **a** $643 - 228$
     b $972 - 557$
     c $754 - 349$
     d $880 - 465$

27 **a** $424 - 278$
     b $735 - 589$
     c $302 - 156$
     d $923 - 767$

28 **a** $578 - 524$
     b $393 - 329$
     c $526 - 472$
     d $842 - 788$

29 **a** $399 - 52$
     b $375 - 18$
     c $383 - 26$
     d $661 - 304$

30 **a** $329 - 66$
     b $357 - 84$
     c $308 - 35$
     d $564 - 291$

31 **a** $232 - 57$
     b $204 - 29$
     c $243 - 78$
     d $371 - 196$

32 **a** $419 - 374$
     b $382 - 327$
     c $241 - 196$
     d $103 - 58$

Find the numbers to replace the * in each of the following.

33   3*2
      45*
 + *23
   1087

34   53*
      *13
 + 2*2
   1079

35   *31
      2*3
 + 61*
   1186

36   8*5
      32*
 + *43
   1298

37   51*
      *42
 + 4*2
   1257

38   8**5
 − *36*
   2623

39   *87*
 − 3**2
   5246

40   9*6*
 − *4*2
   7163

41   *9*8
 − 5*2*
   3408

42   3**9
 − *25*
   2710

43   *96*
 − 3**5
   6842

44   4*9*
 − *5*0
   377

Example 17

Find the numbers to replace the * in each of the following.

a
$$\begin{array}{r} *7 \\ \times\ 5 \\ \hline 135 \end{array}$$

b
$$\begin{array}{r} 1*8 \\ \times\ 5 \\ \hline 590 \end{array}$$

c
$$6)\overline{***}\ \ 36$$

Here are the completed answers.

a
$$\begin{array}{r} 27 \\ \times\ 5 \\ \hline 135 \end{array}$$
because $135 \div 5 = 27$

b
$$\begin{array}{r} 118 \\ \times\ 5 \\ \hline 590 \end{array}$$
because $590 \div 5 = 118$

c
$$6)\overline{216}\ \ 36$$
because $36 \times 6 = 216$

Exercise 9.16

1 356×4 **2** 253×5 **3** 134×9
4 240×8 **5** 405×3 **6** 203×7
7 215×12 **8** 105×30

Find the 'odd answer out' for questions **9** to **14**.

9 a 189×8
   b 216×7
   c 257×6
   d 168×9

10 a 178×7
   b 144×9
   c 162×8
   d 216×6

11 a 192×5
   b 140×7
   c 240×4
   d 320×3

12 a 392×6
   b 294×8
   c 336×7
   d 262×9

13 a 156×12
   b 117×16
   c 134×14
   d 104×18

14 a 180×21
   b 115×32
   c 135×28
   d 105×36

15 $693 \div 3$ **16** $864 \div 4$ **17** $655 \div 5$
18 $988 \div 4$ **19** $618 \div 3$ **20** $910 \div 7$
21 $186 \div 6$ **22** $198 \div 9$

Find the 'odd answer out' for questions **23** to **28**.

23 a $399 \div 3$
   b $492 \div 4$
   c $738 \div 6$
   d $861 \div 7$

24 a $928 \div 8$
   b $756 \div 6$
   c $812 \div 7$
   d $580 \div 5$

25 a $512 \div 4$
   b $896 \div 7$
   c $384 \div 3$
   d $540 \div 5$

26 a $432 \div 6$
   b $576 \div 8$
   c $511 \div 7$
   d $648 \div 9$

27 a $1620 \div 12$
   b $2720 \div 20$
   c $2040 \div 15$
   d $3400 \div 25$

28 a $2250 \div 18$
   b $3000 \div 24$
   c $4340 \div 35$
   d $4500 \div 36$

Find the numbers to replace the * in each of the following.

29
$$\begin{array}{r} *8 \\ \times\ 4 \\ \hline 192 \end{array}$$

30
$$\begin{array}{r} 3* \\ \times\ 8 \\ \hline 256 \end{array}$$

31
$$\begin{array}{r} 1*2 \\ \times\ 3 \\ \hline 396 \end{array}$$

32
$$\begin{array}{r} *18 \\ \times\ 4 \\ \hline 872 \end{array}$$

33
$$\begin{array}{r} 13* \\ \times\ 5 \\ \hline 670 \end{array}$$

34
$$5)\overline{***}\ \ 75$$

35
$$9)\overline{***}\ \ 68$$

36
$$5)\overline{***}\ \ 125$$

37
$$3)\overline{***}\ \ 242$$

38
$$4)\overline{***}\ \ 208$$

39
$$6)\overline{***}\ \ 120$$

40
$$9)\overline{***}\ \ 90$$

Exercise 9.17

1 In the picture below, the table, the television, and the lamp are all of equal height.

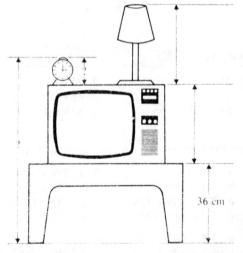

36 cm

a How high is the top of the lamp above the floor?

b The height of the lamp is three times the height of the clock.
What is the height of the clock?

c How high is the top of the clock above the floor?

2 The summit of Ben Nevis is 1343 m above sea level.
  a What is the height of Scafell Pike if its summit is 361 m lower?
  b Find the height of Mount Everest if it is nine times higher than Scafell Pike.

3 A carton full of eggs weighs 425 g and the empty carton weighs 35 g.
  If there are 6 eggs in the carton, what is the weight of each egg?

4 A boy has a bag containing 32 marbles each of which weighs 9 g.
  If the empty bag weighs 12 g, what is the weight of the full bag?

5 The distance from London to Peterborough by rail is 125 km.

  a If Edinburgh is 5 times further away from London than Peterborough, what is the distance from London to Edinburgh?
  b If it is 191 km from Newcastle to Edinburgh, how far is it from London to Newcastle?
  c If Newcastle is twice as far from London as Retford, what is the distance from London to Retford?
  d If the distance from Edinburgh to Aberdeen is the same as that from London to Retford, how far is it from London to Aberdeen?

6 The height of St. Paul's Cathedral is 112 m. What is the height of the Empire State Building in New York if it is 4 times taller? What is the height of the Eiffel Tower in Paris if it is 129 m shorter than the Empire State Building?

7 The population of Shaftesbury is 4080, which is 5490 less than that of Sherborne.
  What is the population of Sherborne?
  If the population of Sherborne is 3 times greater than that of Blandford Forum, what is the population of Blandford Forum?
  If the population of Blandford Forum is 11 times greater than that of Buckhorn Weston, what is the population of Buckhorn Weston?

8 A railway tunnel has two vertical shafts for ventilation, and the distance between them is the same as the distance from either shaft to the nearer end of the tunnel.
  If the length of the tunnel is 1410 m, what is the distance between the shafts?
  If the distance between the shafts is 5 times the depth of either shaft, what is the depth of either shaft?

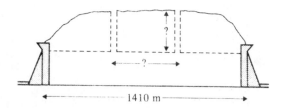

9 A boy has a bag filled with marbles which weighs 235 g. The empty bag weighs 25 g. The bag contains 5 large marbles and 15 smaller ones. If each large marble weighs 18 g, what is the weight of each small marble?